Twiggy
Woman

Twiggy Woman

First published by Skein Press in 2023.
skeinpress.com

A CIP catalogue for this title is available from the British Library.

ISBN 978-1-915017-07-9

Cover design and layout: Patrick Fisher for Frontwards Design
Cover image: Helena Grimes

Printed by L&C Printing Group, Poland
The paper in this book was produced using pulp from managed forests.

Skein Press gratefully acknowledges the financial support it receives
from the Arts Council.

Skein Press is also grateful for the support it receives from the Rowan
Trust, Dublin UNESCO City of Literature, Dublin City Council and the
Department of Children, Equality, Disability, Integration, and Youth.

Comhairle Cathrach
Bhaile Átha Cliath
Dublin City Council

An Roinn Leanaí, Comhionannais,
Míchumais, Lánpháirtíochta agus Óige
Department of Children, Equality,
Disability, Integration and Youth

Twiggy Woman

ghostly folktales by
Oein
DeBhairduin

illustrated by
Helena
Grimes

For all those who
have lived amongst the
monsters and were kind
enough to share their
tales with me. I hope I
do you justice.

Acknowledgements

To my loyal readers and supporters and to the Arts Council, which was kind enough to fund the commission of this work, thank you for giving space so that tales largely unknown, but lived, can find another way to be in the world.

To Helena Grimes, whose creative offerings and insights have taken my imaginings and given them such a potent form on paper. I have so enjoyed your skill and individual vision in letting the story tell itself through your own gifts.

To Gráinne O'Toole, Nidhi Zak/Aria Eipe and Mahito Indi Henderson – thank you for both listening and hearing me. A very sincere and special thank you to Fionnuala Cloke, who helped me navigate the sometimes stormy seas of creativity amidst a busy life, and for trusting that this boat of words would make its way to a safe harbour. You are a calm and steady Northern Star as an editor and very much a valued friend.

To Willie by the fire, Pink Mary among the pine trees, Davey by the bog side, Old Lawrence by the pebbledash wall, to my fellow young rangers staring at the stars through the yellowed plastic skylight, to a precious friend in the conference room of a midlands hotel, and, as always, to the old man himself, Owenie, I thank you all for the stories in this collection.

And last, but never least, to the bini komra Chester and Dan, mo gra, you make me fearless x

Author's note

Ghosts and ghouls are a part of all our childhoods in one way or another. I didn't grow up with a terror of the bogeyman, who was such a strong and pervasive presence in the lives and night-time worries of my buffer friends, although I knew of him and his nightmarish workings. Instead I grew up with other creatures of terror, most of whom were more direct, intimate and knowing.

Stories and the act of storytelling have remained sacred and vital in our community. As Mincéirí, when we encounter unfathomable judgement from strangers or neighbours, when cruelty becomes so normal and injustice is left uncorrected and unacknowledged, the mind and spirit can find many ways to make sense of the senseless, and stories are a tool in this process. Knowing that harsh experiences have a shared context in your community allows the loneliness of rejection, the pain of loss and the sting of injustice to become a bridge of shared connection. I can't, in truth, tell you the very first ghost story I was told, for my youth and adolescence were filled with a mash and mush of it, all from the elders around me. Tales were a way for them to frame and explain trauma, grief and loss and, at the same time, the fantastical horror of them could dilute the impact of the real-life monsters.

Traumas don't fall on stones but can cling to the lives of those who experience them and trickle down to the generations that rise after them. Pain and loss are processed in a way that can be tolerated – in stories of vengeful creatures, of malevolent fairies, of disembodied voices and resentful spirits, tales full of warning and risk. This process is one shared with cultures and communities across the globe, but within the Traveller context, it provides shelter in a continuing onslaught of horrors.

Eerie stories bring with them slivers of wisdom about how to engage with the unexpected. They provide a map in times of fear to aid navigation through bewildering experiences. They teach us what is important, for tales that orientate around loss show what is precious. They not only reveal the otherworld but show us the threads of connection between our mundane outer lives and our deeper inner world, in which we are much bigger, wilder and weirder than we outwardly appear.

I've always found darker stories deeply intriguing. The openness to being frightened while knowing on some level that we are still safe is shared by most people and goes beyond the boundaries of culture. Most of us relish the opportunity to let the mind wander into fearful corners, in the comfort of knowing we won't be left there. There are a few rare situations where we allow ourselves to be vulnerable and to suspend disbelief, and listening to a storyteller recount a terror-filled plight is one of the oldest. It allows us to catch a glimpse of a wider-held shared fear, and to know more about ourselves and the world.

There are stories we want to tell and pass on and then there are stories that demand to be told. I had to search for some of the stories in this collection; others came to me unexpectedly, and there was a relief for those tellers in that unburdening, as they fulfilled their responsibility of passing along the tale. Some of the stories are old, knotted in lore and cross connections, of people, place and power. Some are newer, having only landed on the ears of a few, and are well on their way to joining the cultural canon of our literature and storytelling.

Above all, stories are meant to entertain and distract, and scary stories can chill the bones, stir the mind and awaken old spirits.

May these stories be a feast of fright for you.

The evil eye
A gammy suwn'r

There are worlds that live in us all, those spaces of thought and recall, of fierce fancy and fables, of driven convictions and firm ideals. This is where we spin the tales that make us and explore the retellings of events in our lives. Of the wild spirits, the upper choirs and the earthly griwogs, there is the other plain, the inner one, of the mind, where horror can be born, formed, untangled and undone.

This tale came to me recently in a hushed tone at the end of a community conference. The brief privacy of a near-empty room, while the other guests went to get food, gave us shelter for the sharing. It arose from a conversation earlier that day about the trials of the inner world and how we each, in our own way, traverse that landscape between health, healing and harm and how knowing the world, only through a single lens, in itself does not always give the answers that might be sought. I promised to keep her name secret but I can share her story, and I hope this retelling does it justice. Culturally, being overlooked is a terrible thing, but sometimes being seen can be truly terrifying.

Some of the most disturbing things in life, I believe, are not those that come when we are on the watch for them, but those that intrude into the everyday world, making strange the so-called normal. When we think of hauntings, we often think of the ghouls that stalk the lanes and byways at night, of dark evenings and winds that gale and cry out in lost voices, or sometimes the souls of those stolen away by cruel acts. What lore and legend tell us, however, is that hauntings come in many forms. Sometimes it's the land that is tormented, or there is a wound that refuses to heal or a scar that is forever picked at unknowingly by the actions of those who share that space. Other times it might be an object of significance upon which a spirit lingers. Very rarely, it is on a person.

Ellen and Martin had married in May and the day had been so wonderfully bright that the service in the church was bathed in shades of splendid colour as the light streamed through the stained-glass windows.

That evening, after the photographs had been taken and the guests had sat for food and the sharing of music, the skies opened to thunderous crackles and a deluge of rain.

'It's a blessing,' said Ellen's mother as she turned from the window. 'Sure, even the angels are crying out with joy for you both.' And she nodded to the well-stocked fire at the end of the banquet hall, which was as warm as the outpouring of affection for the couple from all those who were gathered in celebration.

The only sadness in Ellen was that she must up her own life and move to the place of her new husband, which was a custom his people still held. While she knew she would never be too far from her own, this new stage of life brought both excitement and a sliver of sadness. When one welcomes the thaw of spring, the silver of the woods can still be missed.

Their first home was a small trailer on the edge of the camp. It was a bit overlooked as the path that cut through the molly curled along the eastern side of the trailer, but with the sycamore tree being their closest neighbour, it was still an intimate space for them. They were happy and hopeful.

One day, some months after their wedding day, Ellen had just gotten home from the shop and dropped the heavy, food-laden bags on the floor. Her mind was busy with thoughts of dinner and the phone call she'd promised to her sister. She opened the press to put away the messages and discovered, in the centre of the middle shelf, a gruesome sight – a human eye, round and blood-soaked, awash with a dripping pink pus, sitting in a pool of crimson. While it did not move, she knew it was looking right at her, as if captivated. It stared, unflinching. Her own eyes saw it and she knew she had been seen by it.

A scream roared from her and she snapped the doors of the cabinet shut, taking some steps back. Her hands became a guard upon her mouth, trying to capture in vain the cries that rose after. Martin rushed in, eyes wide and full of worry. He grasped Ellen's shoulders with his hands and steadied her shaking.

'What?' jumped from his lips.

'The press! There's an eye! There's an eye! There's . . . an . . . eye!' Ellen screamed, heart full of flutter, gesturing to the now-closed cabinet.

Martin, with his hand trembling, reached out and slowly opened the door of the press. He craned his head around the edge of the door, his eyes darting left and right and then quickly away. Soon the press door was fully open and the shelf that had held that macabre organ contained nothing but the usual tins and stores of food.

'Ellen, what are you talking about?' sputtered Martin as he patted the wooden shelves.

'There was an eye. I saw an eye,' Ellen shot back.

'Well, if there was,' Martin said, eyes lifted to the ceiling of the trailer, 'it's gone now.'

He shook his head and returned to the small patch of garden in front of the caravan. Ellen, still rattled by the gruesome sight, was overcome with shock and annoyance that her husband had simply moved on.

Ellen rested against the sink with a clear view of the trailer's larder, still not quite believing what she had seen. Her mind scanned the last few days, weeks and months of her life and she recognised that there had been some points of stress. 'To the doctor I'll take myself,' she promised, as she shook off the moment and lined her tins of food and loaves of bread on the small worktop space beside the sink.

The next morning, she rose early and sat on a chair by the open trailer door, welcoming in the morning chorus as she sipped hot sweet tea and looked tenderly at the new red cord that was twisted and knotted tightly upon her wrist. Martin had given it to her late the night before. 'For protection and for not being overlooked,' he had whispered to her as they were about to drift off to sleep, both glad to have taken some action, rather than having only words to bring balm to their fear.

The gore in the cupboard seemed vague, less real and softer in recall. She would plan a calm day to mind herself. The notion of visiting her doctor left her as soon as she had drunk the last drop from her cup. The days that followed were mostly uneventful and the busyness of life drew her mornings in and nights out, and soon the experience was all but forgotten.

Some weeks later, Ellen was in town when her path crossed that of an old friend. They were so happy to see each other that they decided to go for lunch to catch up – a rare treat for Ellen – and thankfully they found a welcoming café quickly. They took a small table in the quiet but friendly coffee shop and, in the ease of the soft music that wafted through the café, they sat, shared and ate.

As the conversation was drawing to an end with promises of a reunion again soon, the soup in the bowl from which Ellen had been sipping suddenly gurgled and splashed. Expecting the cause to be a slipped spoon, she saw instead that there floated the eye. That same eye with its cold blue iris looking back at her as it bobbed in the rcmaining soup like a buoy at sea.

Ellen shrieked and with the twist of her hand upturned the bowl and sent it flying across the room, where it landed with a sharp crash, the last of the soup splattering against the wall and floor. She rose with such force that her chair was thrown back. She stood there in horror as the guests and staff turned to look at her in bewilderment. As a waiter rushed over with a cloth in hand, Ellen turned to her friend, who looked at her with worry.

'I saw . . . I saw . . .' murmured Ellen, catching her breath, 'an eye!'

Her friend's face creased in consternation and, tilting her head, she moved slowly to inspect the spray of soup. Neither turning to apologise nor say goodbye, Ellen grabbed her jacket and hurried to her car. As horrified as she was by the incident, she also felt the sharp burn of mortification.

As she drove to the surgery, her heart was beating like ferocious waves against a storm-ravaged shore. Blessing herself and humming out prayers as the glistening onyx rosary beads swung left to right from the rear-view mirror, she tried to breathe in sync with their movement to calm herself. She arrived at the surgery but she wasn't yet convinced she would go in. She hovered outside. As she worked up the courage to go in, she gripped the door handle and pushed it open a few inches.

How could she explain to a doctor what had happened? 'I'm not going mad!' Ellen said out loud before silencing herself, realising that talking to herself and claiming not to be mad might just be the thing that people who've looser ties to sanity might do.

The reception room was spartan, except for the flyers stacked on the coffee table, which was flanked by rows of chairs. The air was filled with the scent of pine and chlorine. She would have preferred a softer space, more welcoming and friendly, for the conversation that was to follow. She sat nervously, picking the cuticles of her fingernails, until the voice of the receptionist cut through the light daydream that Ellen had found herself in.

'Ellen, the doctor can see you now.'

Ellen shuffled into the doctor's room with a sense of tiredness nibbling at her bones. The event had shaken her greatly.

The doctor listened patiently as Ellen told her about the eye, the fright she had been given and the worries it had raised in her and waited for the doctor to roll out a judgement. Instead, to Ellen's surprise, the doctor inquired about her home life, her general health, her family, how long a night she slumbered and what food she ate. She left with a plan – more sleep and some medication for anxiety, but mostly an affirmation that her sight, rather than being supernatural, might just be her mind whispering an understanding she was not yet ready to face.

As she drove home, she decided to call into her local church, light some candles and take solace in the peace of the place. She sat in the front row, her feet firmly planted against the mosaic tiles to ground herself. Before the image of the Virgin of Perpetual Hope, with its thick gold rimmed frame, she sat praying and thinking of her journey over the last while. After some time a nun passed by and, sensing her worry, sat beside her. The nun didn't give her name. She was old, having skin like the cratered bark of a sun-worn tree and a voice that crackled like an open fire. Ellen asked for a blessing and the old nun said she would say a prayer for her, but for now, they would sit together, in the stillness of the moment as the lit candles burned.

That night as the dusk rushed in and Ellen returned to her bed, she breathed a great sigh of relief. The days that followed, however, brought with them little solace. For the ghastly eye had not departed despite the medical counsel and spiritual intervention. Often she would drink from her cup of morning tea to find that eye floating on the surface. It would roll out of shoes as she was getting dressed. Once, as she fumbled with some keys to unlock a press, there the eye was, bulging out of the keyhole, staring back at her.

As often as the eye looked at her, Ellen could not make herself confront it. Every time it came into view, she would screw her eyes shut so tightly that flashes of red and white would flare behind her eyelids. Each time the eye visited, her world became smaller and smaller. She didn't want to go anywhere, so as not to give the eye more scope. In her own home she knew where to look and where not to look, sometimes spending hours with the curtains shut and the lights off. Even if the eye was there, if she couldn't see it, then perhaps its gaze wasn't fixed upon her.

Martin, grew increasingly worried for his wife. One morning, seeing her untouched cup of tea and the trailer door shutting out the birdsong she once loved so much, he suggested she go to the home of her sister. On her arrival the family was alarmed to see how Ellen looked, so diminished and distressed, with hair hardly washed and mismatched clothes. They did not know that she dressed in the dark, lived her days inside, trying to shut out the gaze of the eye. She promised to stay a few nights. Spending time and playing with her nieces and nephews would bring renewed joy to her heart.

While still not knowing what had taken place, but understanding a great strain was on Ellen, her sister filled her a deep, piping-hot bath, sprinkled with lavender oil and chamomile petals. Ellen fell asleep in the bathtub and, on waking, thought the room a bit darker. The lightbulb, still on, shone dimmer, as if invisible hands had a hold upon it. She unplugged the bath and rose to get her towel. There, at the bottom of the bath, sat the disembodied eye, still dripping wet and oozing, its gaze fixed.

So tired, this time Ellen did not scream nor shout. Exhausted by the months of terror, she felt for the first time the bile rise, and a cold anger finally unleashed itself in her. She did not flinch, instead she reached out, picked up the eye and crushed it between her trembling fingers. Its fluids poured out in a loud, prolonged squelch as she tightened her grasp, determined not to be haunted by this presence any longer. When she finally relaxed her grip and decided to inspect the remains of her tormentor, her hand was bare but for some of the remaining bubbles from the bathwater.

The eye has never returned, and Ellen has slowly found her love of life again, of cups of weéd in the company of the morning chorus and walks on the woodland trails. She tries not to think of the eye and has learned not to look too long in dark corners. She dares not delve into the meaning of it all, in case she invites the eye back into her life. She has found a peaceful acceptance of experiencing something both real and surreal, and her ultimate command over both. There is strength and wisdom in her acceptance of the unknowable and in her gratitude for both learning this lesson and having grasped her personal power.

Bloody finger

Moillhas liba

One morning on our way to school my older brother, Darrell, and I stopped in front of an empty house that stood at the corner of Liam Mellows Street. The house was in disrepair, and this stirred our childish curiosity. The windows had slats of wood nailed irregularly across the frames, leaving gaps but tight enough to bar any entry. The building was dressed in ivy that stretched from the foundations to the roof, where tiles had lifted with age, weather and the reaching vines. The door was a mottled brown, its once shiny polish cracked and splintered by biting frost and searing summer suns. The brass door handle was covered in a thick layer of grime; it was a long time since there had been company in that home. We peered through a gap between the slats of wood into the front room, part interest and part unspoken dare, to see what lay inside.

The old tenants, long gone, had been replaced with mice and spiders who kept it as their home. The room was small, a narrow cast-iron fire place in the corner with a yellow porcelain-tiled surround. The wallpaper had mostly peeled off the walls and was spread across the floor like the darkened skins of old bananas. The room was bare. A single chair stood facing the window, no more than four feet away from us. It was shabby and worn, roughest at the tips of the armrests where the fabric had worn away, stained a darker shade on its tall back by, I imagined, the greasy hair of whoever once owned it.

Suddenly a woman appeared seated on the chair. She

didn't slowly come into view. No, she was simply there having not been there the second before. Her arrival shocked us into silence, breaking the free flow of our conversation, and neither shout nor breath passed our lips. She was short and plump, with a fleshy face, sunken along the jaw as if she carried neither tooth nor smile, resembling a crumbling Halloween pumpkin. The door to the room remained closed, so she hadn't entered that way. All of a sudden she was right in front of us, her bulbous nose pressed firm to the window pane, her eyes milky and unfocused, twitching as if to try to catch a glimpse of us. If she was of mortal flesh, moving at such a speed from chair to window she would have crashed through the glass. It was only then that we screamed.

We quickly left and rushed home rather than continue on our way to school. Our heads were full of horror and our tongues loud with the experience. Our father, amused by the idea of it all, maybe suspecting that we'd been up to some mischief, took us back to the house, surveyed the room and the empty chair, and quickly sent us on our way to class.

Darrell and I have spoken of the vision often since, and while I never saw her again, Darrell swears he has seen her, from time to time, out of the corner of his eye. Once at the bottom of the hill as the road turns, and once more through the spaces between moving traffic as she stood across the road from him, before disappearing.

When I think of the old woman, 'Bloody fingers' is the story that comes to mind, one that has passed through our family like an heirloom. It was first told to us by Owenie, my father, the long night of the day on which we saw the old woman.

The wind howled loud outside the wattle-framed tent, rustling the creases of the thick canvas. John and Martin took warmth from a skillet pot with a heavy lid that rested at the foot of their straw bed. Filled with fire coals, the pot had seen a long life of cooking food and feeding the family. But now it had a jagged crack running from lip to the foot of one of its knobbly legs and was reused as a warmer to stave off the bitter winds and the deep night-time frost. The subleens were snuggled tight beneath the protective warmth of their mink blankets.

John was ten, an age he was proud of. He had decided the year before to leave 'and a half' behind. That's what little children say, he thought. He was taller than most children his age, his head already level with his father's shoulder. He had hair sandy like the beach of Culleenamore and deep blue eyes like its waters. John had a heart for laughter and a mind for mischief. While he never wanted to cause harm, he found himself all too often in all sorts of devilment.

Martin, the younger of the two, was eight. He was often an unwilling accomplice in John's escapades out of love, loyalty and sometimes curiosity, but he had a quieter disposition and a gentler way with people. He was calm and thoughtful, with a head full of dreams and a spirit overflowing with empathy. His little face was covered in freckles like tiny flecks of pollen, and tufts of deep-brown hair danced around his head. He kept in his heart the wild hopes and imagination of youth, which shone brightly from his curious eyes. He had taken to wearing his brother's old shoes, which were two sizes too big for him, so they clopped and flopped as he walked, and every now and then he would tie the laces of them under and over the shoe to make them steady. He never minded though; they were soft enough on the road as they journeyed that he never paid too much attention to how they looked.

Their mother, Mary, poked her head through the canvas fold at the entrance to the tent and whispered to them kind words of rest and sleep, for the morning after would be a long one, with their travels to Sligo town and a stay for the harvest markets. She was a plump woman with thick bark-brown hair that she twisted up into a high bun at the peak of her head. By the evening half the locks and wisps of her mane would burst out of the bun and dangle about her face and shoulders.

Smiles spread across their faces at the mention of Sligo,

for that was the place of kind people, especially Old Miss Gaynor, and it was the place of the tallest horse chestnut trees that they had ever seen, and conker season had arrived.

They rose and took to the road, walking while the sun still rested in its own bed. The journey to Sligo was soft and felt short as they carried with them the company of songs. They arrived as the sun was about to set that very same day, and the molly was quickly pulled to form.

Next morning, with the rising sun thawing the silver out of the landscape, John and Martin made fleet steps down the well-trodden road to Old Miss Gaynor's home. Her house was a small one set on the edge of a quiet grove. It had a thatched roof and tiny squat windows that let in only a few rays of light, but let out little warmth from her fire.

While her nearest neighbours, almost half a mile away, had roofs of slate and tile, she was perfectly happy with the rows of dried corn and rushes that gave her shelter, and she was quick to extend that shelter to anyone she met.

One winter, many years before, the boys' family had passed by her home on a dark and dreary evening, and she made sure there was a place at her table for them, an extra sod on the fire and a dry bed for the night. Every year since, the family made sure to call to her as they passed through town, with bundles of news from far away, tales of marriages, fortunes lost and won, and reports of who had a new bonnie child in the world.

Martin, although he was smaller, was the swifter of the

two and reached the door of Old Miss Gaynor's first. He let three hard loud knocks fall on the space above the handle, and shouted excitedly, 'We're here!' Turning to his brother, he rocked back and forth on the balls of his feet, thinking about what delights Old Miss Gaynor might have for them. Last time she served them fresh roasted apples from the fire, lightly dripped with honey.

However, instead of a warm welcome from the woman of the house, he heard only silence. As soon as John had made his way to the door, he too knocked, louder and more clearly, and the sound of it seemed to echo back to them from within.

Still no reply.

Out of curiosity and thinking that Old Miss Gaynor might be asleep in her bed, they took a peek through the window into the living room and noticed that the fire was out, not a glow of warmth from any ember. This was a surprise to them, for it was autumn and to keep warm was not only a wise thing but a duty for someone of her age.

Martin decided to try the handle of the door. One quick turn and it creaked open.

'Miss Gaynor?' said Martin, louder than his usual speaking voice but he hoped not so loud as to frighten or alarm anyone. 'Miss Gaynor, it's Martin and John, Mary and Jackeen's sons. We've come to tell you about our year.'

The words went out but there came back no reply.

With soft steps they made their way to the living room.

There was a light smattering of dust on everything, not obvious at first, as if a fresh loaf of wheaten bread had been baked on the grill and the offering up of flour had not been swept away. Something was uneasy in the room. While they didn't speak to each other of their growing concern, they heard the growls of disquiet in the depths of each other's stomachs.

Martin opened the door to the bedroom, which was off the living room, but then stepped back, thinking it too far an intrusion into Old Miss Gaynor's privacy, but John let the toes of his shoe stop the bedroom door from closing and stepped in. Martin followed so as not to be left on his own. They moved with light feet, feeling in each movement how this space was not their space, heavy with the worry of offending she who owned this home.

Their sight adjusted quickly enough in the darkness and they saw Miss Gaynor tucked up tight in her bed. As they stepped closer they saw that her shawl, always wrapped about her head, was intact, her eyes were closed and her lips were gently meeting. At first they thought she was resting, lost in her own dreams. Then they noticed the stillness of her chest and realised it was no slumber. Her lifeless features were not ajar like many of the deceased. They were soft. She was at peace.

Martin let out a long, deep exhale. The wheeze of his lungs trailed out, filling the room with a hushed whisper. His head snapped towards his brother, whose face was pale, mouth wide with an withheld gasp. They stood, eyes locked on Old Miss Gaynor.

After a time, John tapped his foot against Martin's leg and nodded his head forward. At first Martin did not understand, but tap after tap the sight that John had intended came into view. On the left hand of Miss Gaynor, on her index finger, was a large red-stoned ring. Martin wondered how he had never noticed it before but dismissed the thought with a quick shake of his head. If he had been looking for it, he would have seen it, but he never was. His heart jumped at the realisation that John might once again draw them both into mischief. While Martin was usually a willing accomplice in John's escapades, this was a scheme too far. His mind had been flooded with thoughts of how to explain how they were in the house in the first place. Now the heaviness of this new worry about John's devilment pulled at his thoughts. What excuses could they conjure if they went any further?

Looking sidelong at his better-behaved brother, John kissed the back of his fist in a prayer and reached out and touched Old Miss Gaynor's hand as if in a parting gesture of respect, allowing the tip of his nail to catch the edge of the ring. It fell off her finger. John was startled at how easily it had become dislodged, expecting it to have been tight on her finger from years of wearing it. It landed on the floor by the bed with a clunk and spun on the hardwood floorboards, luring John closer. Glints of haw-red caught in the few rays of light in the room. He stared, transfixed by the spinning jewel.

Martin swooped down and picked it up but, nervous of touching her limp hand, he hesitated rather than put it back. John, always the braver of the two, snatched it from him and wavered between what was right and keeping the unexpected prize. His fingers curled around the gem and his mind was filled with ideas of what he could trade or sell it for. A new horse, he thought, or a nice pair of shoes for the village dance, maybe that fine coat he had seen in the window of Murphy's on Main Street. Without thinking much more he slipped the ring into his pocket and made for the door.

'Ah, John,' said Martin, 'you can't be taking that. There'd be scandal in it, John, stealing from an old woman who never did an ounce of harm to anyone.'

John was staring at the ring as if its very force was drawing him in. He scrunched his face, and with his grasp on the handle of the bedroom door, he turned back, muttering, 'There'll be no talk as who would know? I never saw that ring before and you won't be letting any word of it pass between your teeth.'

'We'll raise the alarm so, but nothing about the ring,' said Martin, knowing John would not be swayed.

Swinging the bedroom door wide, John was swift to cross the living room and go out the front door. Martin followed and gently lowered the latch, feeling they had disturbed the place enough.

The brothers did not speak as they made their way down the lane from the house, letting the tension of shame and anger do the talking between them. John was still determined, but disgruntled with himself. Martin tutted and sighed, his only way of giving voice to his annoyance and disappointment. As they walked, the lane seemed longer than before, as if it was stretching with each step. After a while, however, they realised they were not any closer to the edge of the woods. They thought that they must have taken a wrong turn somewhere, a confusing idea indeed, as the lane to Old Miss Gaynor's home was mostly a straight one.

Suddenly a scream tore through the sky above the trees, shaking the birds from their nests and many a leaf from its branch. Both boys cradled their heads in their hands, palms tight against their ears to block out the long wail that seemed to draw on and on until an unnatural silence fell. It was as if the woods themselves had been emptied of all animals and not even the grass could rustle in the wind.

Crack! went the trunk of a tree that stood beside John, sending long sharp splinters into the air, forcing the boys backwards. The woody shards left trails of fresh blood across the boys' little arms, their stunned faces wincing in shock as the slivers shot passed them. As the brothers gained back their footing, they stood, mouths wide in awe. The tree had been split in two, leaving branch and bark all about and wood dust in the air.

Martin looked at his brother, and with his breath

bundled up into his chest, took a big leap away from him. For now he could see what had caused the tree to fall.

There beside John was a long snake-like creature, twisting and coiling as it rose threateningly higher above him. Serpentine and rising, it jolted as it moved. The realisation of what it was danced across Martin's mind.

It was a finger, long and growing, monstrous, with flesh pale and stretched taut over the thin bones that thrusted beneath it. It grew longer and longer, a long grey blade at its tip, moving higher above the brothers. It curved back, like the loop of a whip about to strike.

'Run, John, run!' screamed Martin as he gestured with both hands to the side of his brother, who now too could see the grotesque finger that hovered above them. As soon as the brothers' feet moved, down came the finger and struck deep into the ground, tossing soil and stone aside.

The brothers fled, and as they ran, the finger followed, growing ever longer as it reached out to strike at them. It tore through trees and bushes, crashed against the stone and boulders as they scuttled away from it. The brothers screamed and cried and ran, all the muscles of their legs burning from effort, but the woods had become endless and the finger seemed to be ever growing, wrapping itself at times around trees as if to bar the way back.

When they had a chance to catch their breath, they took it. The finger and its lethal nail were still in view but seemed to have slowed, as if it was growing in confidence that it would have their blood.

They trembled and shook with fear, their breaths rushing in and out of them like a storm. John, bent over from exhaustion, realised what was behind the finger's attack. It was the ring. He had taken the ring from a finger of Old Miss Gaynor's dead hand and that finger wanted it back. 'I'll give it back, Martin. I'll give it back! I swear, I swear!' he cried, tears rushing down his face like winter rain against a window.

The brothers turned in the direction of Old Miss Gaynor's home and sprinted past the finger as it swooped and struck at them, almost catching them several times. Ravenous and raging, it struck and struck but each time the brothers were just out of its reach.

Soon the house was in view and the sight of it gave fresh energy to the brothers as they ran like hares towards it. As soon as they were inside, they slammed the door shut, snapping off the finger just beneath the hinge where it had pushed itself through. They rushed to the bedside of Old Miss Gaynor and, begging and crying, pushed the ring into the palm of her cold, stiff hand, promising never to steal again or let another steal, and explaining what good lives they would live and what Masses they would have said in her memory.

As they kneeled beside her, wailing and praying, the room grew darker, and a small sliver of light that had pierced itself into the room from a gap in the drawn curtains began to flicker and move across the walls and floors, casting a shadow in the form of the old woman. The shadow seemed to chitter and chatter in words that they couldn't understand but which they knew to be taunting.

'We're taken, Martin, we're taken!' John roared into the ceiling as it grew closer and closer. The brothers crushed their eyes closed in wait of the inevitable as the shadow grew and began to envelop them.

Silence fell.

The boys opened their eyes and the room was at peace, as it was when they first arrived. Struggling to their feet, blessing themselves as they rose, they took deep breaths as a sense of calm returned to the room. They looked at Old Miss Gaynor, still in her bed, still peaceful and with the ring now back on her finger, which was again its usual length. The tip, however was bloodied and raw from striking at the brothers.

Still apologising, the brothers left the bedroom, straightening their clothes as they went. Martin opened the front door and was relieved that the road home was now in sight. As he crossed the threshold, he looked back at his brother, their eyes meeting intensely, and with a sharp nod of his head, Martin urged him to crush-auin.

'I'm coming,' replied John, lifting his foot to step out, when the door, moved by unseen hands, slammed tightly shut, locking John in, his screams blowing out from around its edges.

And then there was silence.

Twiggy woman
Bini shako a beoir

When I was eight, myself and my older brother, Darrell, along with ten other subleens, went on a camping trip to Glassilaun Beach with the youth group with which my father was working and some other parents and workers.

We travelled in a rickety maroon minibus. We were told they had selected maroon as it was the county colour of Galway, the tribal lands, but it was far more likely that it was chosen because of its low price. The rear window was held in place with lashings of glue, thick as frozen honey, and strips of dull steel tape. I remember watching that window vibrate as we travelled along the roads and boreens, expecting it to eventually jolt up and out as we bounced over potholes and swung roughly around corners. It never did.

We wore forest-green jumpers with an eagle motif above the words 'The Young Rangers' and we were ready for adventure. The day was a fresh one, and we explored the land, made a fire, watched the men come in from fishing and drew dreams yet to be dreamt along the downy sands of the beach. But the night came in with a howl.

Three large tents had been set up and our water bottles filled from the fireside kettle. We wormed into our sleeping bags, adding a pile of blankets on top. Two of the tents stood the weariness of the weather that night. Ours, the third, did not.

It started with a small leak that appeared in the middle of the arched canvas. We managed to catch the rain at first with a cup from a flask, which we would take turns

44

to lift and empty outside the tent each time it filled. The tear slowly spread, and deep in the night, when most of us were on the cusp of slumber, a sudden downpour of rain flooded the tent like a waterfall, gushing all about us as we jumped to our feet in our sleeping bags, like well-bundled chrysalises.

In the giddy laughter and excitement of it all, we took refuge in the minibus, folding down seats to make beds, wringing out towels, padding down our pillows and drawing our initials and shapes on the bus windows, the warmth of our own breaths making it a midnight canvas.

That is the first night I heard of the twiggy woman, she who comes when she wants and who leaves a deep mark on the lives of those she encounters. Twiggy women are present in the weather-worn trees that grow from wind and seed-will in fields and forests, gardens and roadsides. They hold their own space until they are moved to claim a price from those who are unkind to the most vulnerable, our children.

There wasn't a sole teller, as the tale moved between us all, like a ripple in a pond. I remember lying on my back, listening, as I looked up and out through a small discoloured plastic skylight that sat on top of the minibus like a miniature hat. I was thankful for the company of so many others. That night, and on many of my youthful nights after, I dreamt of her. Never a true nightmare nor a full dream, she was often there, on the edges of slumber, shuffling and doddering into view, only to wander off again.

There once was a home among the green fields of Mallow that held under its shelter a family of four. There was the mother, the father and two kind-hearted children. To their neighbours and wider family they had the blessings of the best of most things, of new clothing, of fresh food, of sweet music and enough books to read that no evening would be without an adventure. What most people did not know nor see was that there was another force within their home, of which they dared not speak.

The father of the family, while proud and of good standing to all those outside of his own front door, was harsh within the home. He had a will as unbending as wrought iron and an anger that smouldered like dried kindling. He was strict to the point of cruelty and expected all things in the home to work like clockwork. Having little patience for mistakes, he was brutal when they happened. He would rage and shout, tear towards his wife and children and swipe at them with sally rods.

At night the mother and children would cry and wrap each other in their sorrows and pain. But in the morning, they would dress themselves with smiles for their neighbours and go about their duties, letting none know that the difference between life inside and life outside was as stark as night to day.

This is how it was for a very long time, until one night, while sitting in her bed, the youngest of the children gazed out her window to the trees and dared to whisper, 'If only someone could help us.' While none within the four walls of the home had heard her plea, someone, something, somewhere, had.

That someone began to move with sluggish steps towards the child's home, her weather-worn leather boots with their frayed seams and loose heels dragging slowly through moist soil, rustling the crumbled leaves and winter debris as she passed. She brought a deep staleness with her, that of ancient bog oak and festered moss. She wore a thick and heavy cloak of tanned leather, smirched with sod and clay, which hung from her bony body like the heavy draperies of a mansion's windows. There was a belt of thin umber twine around her waist, and the cloak's long hood concealed her face. On her back was a wicker basket of twigs she picked up along her travels. Some fell out as she walked, leaving a trail for anyone with the eyes to see to follow. At times, she would stop to sleep, standing against the trunks of trees, holding on to them with her hands. She was so soil-ridden and earth-baked that she could not be distinguished from the tree she leaned against.

A few nights after her plea, the child sat peering out the bedroom window. The light of the crescent moon cut down through the darkness of the night. She noticed a new tree in the garden. She could not tell if it was a fruit tree or a blackthorn. Each time she looked at it, it seemed to get ever nearer and its branches seemed to wave to her. When it was close to her window, she woke her sister and they both watched in fear as the tree drew nearer to the pane, until the outline of the twiggy woman emerged in the light cast from their room. She was tall and angular, her limbs like the branches of a leafless winter tree. Her skin was bark and thick with moss and spiderweb. And she moved as rigidly as the timber she was crafted from. Her feet were a mass of rooty tendrils that spread out and gripped the ground beneath her, pulling her closer to the window and the fearful children.

They called out to their parents and their mother quickly arrived, wrapping herself in her robe, alarmed at the cries from her children. Listening to their tale, she moved toward the window. However, she could not see what the children could, for the veil of age often clouds the eyes. Children with a sight unhampered by age and by assumption see the world for what it is rather than what we expect. She told them it was only the branches of a tree that must have broken off in the night and landed near their bedroom, and the children, wanting that to be true, took solace in her words. She promised that the next day they would take the hatchet to the bundling of branches and make timber for their fire. As she tucked the still-upset children into bed, she kissed their brows and promised them that the night would soon pass and that the morning would brush away their worries.

As soon as she left the room, the children's eyes darted again to the window, hopeful of seeing only tomorrow's kindling, but to their alarm, the twiggy woman now stood with her body pressed against the glass, looking in the window. That shaggy-hooded figure, emptiness where a face should be, two small, white, quartz-like eyes in the darkness, unblinking and piercing.

The figure of bark and wood raised her hand. It was made from branches, entwined with ivy where the veins should be, knuckled with moss and swarthy clumps of dried earth. She reached out and tapped the window with a sharp splinter tip and drew it down along the glass. The movement created a long, sharp, screeching sound that stretched through the air. Soon she was scratching at the bottom of the window frame, trying to work her sharp nails under the lip to raise the window, creating for herself a way into the home.

The children, watching her as she moved, jumped to their feet and drew the curtains tight, as if to ignore her could push her back into the mundane. As soon as they did, the scratching at the window stopped, and in time they dared to peek out through the curtain, their small noses twitching against the cold of the night. The figure was no longer there.

As their dancing hearts began to calm and just as dreams began to overcome them, they heard a different noise. This time it was coming from the front door down the hallway from their bedroom. Petrified, they went under the covers together, pinning the blankets tight to the mattress.

The noise woke their father from his bed and he dashed down the hallway, lighting his way with a tightly held candlestick, while the mother took flight back to the room of her children.

The father saw that the twiggy woman, with tendrils of bark moving and coiling, had pressed herself against the frame of the door and dug her spiky body into it, like sharp teeth against flesh, tearing at the planks that moaned under the pressure of her strength until they eventually split, leaving a large crack through which she tumbled.

She clambered through the crack of the door and began to rise to her feet, and the father immediately knew her from childhood warnings. He knew she had come not for the children, in their innocence, but for him in his enduring cruelty. In his frigid arrogance, he felt no fear and threw the candle at her. She was engulfed in a sudden flame that enveloped and seared into her. Instead of screams, she made crackles, pops, sputters and sizzles, and a deep groan rolled out through the house, shaking every inch of it. The twiggy woman did not become ash, but with her ragged clothing gone, and as the smoke about her thinned, all that remained of her was the charred and glowing skeleton of a tree.

The father took the still-smouldering remains and dug a grave as deep and as wide as that of any man and buried the charred limbs in flaky salt and molten spite. He went back to bed, never going to his wife or children, and cast aside any thoughts of change, for she was gone, and he had no heart for growth nor ear for the sorrows he had wrought upon his family. He slept soundly that night in his bed of cold dispassion. Thinking he would never see her again, nor feel the bite of her ire or the savagery of her anger, he did not soften his voice or relax his tense fist in the days that followed.

What he did not know was that returning her to the land was the worst thing for him to have done, for the soil was busy aiding her resurgence. The fresh rain that fell became the sap of her blood and the sods of clay that had he had thrown upon her were slowly changing, growing and knitting themselves into a new garment for her.

While the twiggy woman was reforming deep in the ground in the months that followed, it became clear to the mother and her children that something was happening within their home; something had been disturbed by the twiggy woman's visit. The bedroom doors would open slightly, just a gap, as if pushed by unseen hands. The kettle was slow to boil and a gathering of crows lined the boundary of the garden. The keys of the home would go missing often, and would be found eventually in places that had been checked many times. Every morning soot was found about the fireplace. And despite every best effort, bread baked would refuse to rise.

While the seasons of the year moved forward, the father and the terror of his temper remained the same. One night, as the home creaked in pity and the children and wife were once again shaking in their bedrooms in fear and dread, the twiggy woman finally woke, and with her woody claws and limbs, she scraped her way to the surface. She burst out through the ground and moved rapidly towards the front door of the home.

This time, instead of scraping and scratching at the frame, she knocked. Clear and clean, rapid and sharp. It was enough to raise the father from his bed while the others remained warm in the arms of slumber. As he opened the door, he calmed his annoyance and plastered a welcoming smile on his face, expecting to meet a neighbour on the other side. On seeing her – the twiggy woman – the light in his eyes and colour in his face began to drain away. He stumbled back in shock at the reappearance of the twiggy woman, who began to shuffle into the house and inch closer to him. As she moved through the hallway, she seemed to grow and stretch with every step, the branches on her back reaching out and filling the edges of the room, some scratching on the ceiling, others reaching down and coiling across the floor and some dragging across the wallpapered walls, catching flecks of paper and leaving trails of sap and bark as she moved.

As they neared the end of the corridor, she became less twiggy woman and more a jolting, twisting, crawling mass of fibre and root, of tangled vines and knotted moss. As the father turned and opened his mouth to scream, she jumped down firm upon him, wrapping each of his limbs with hers until he was engulfed.

The youngest child was the only one to wake from the muffled noises outside the room. She shuffled dozily to the open bedroom door and saw the twiggy woman coiling around her father, his body pressed firm against the threadbare carpet, his mouth gagged by the wet roots. On seeing the lackeen, the twiggy woman reached out towards her. The petrified child was within grasping distance when that gnarled hand shifted and clutched tightly the handle of the door and closed it firmly shut, barring the young child sight of her father. The little one returned to her bed, curled up and waited for the household to wake.

The next morning, the mother turned in her bed to awaken her husband for the day ahead. As her eyes drew open and adjusted to the morning light, she patted his empty pillow. She threw back the blankets and found, instead of her tormentor, just a bundle of twigs laid out in the shape of his body, curled up firm and tight, as if fearful and terror-stricken. The frame of a man, clear in outline but without bone or breath. All that was left was the bundling and a warning: sometimes monstrous spirits come for children, other times spirits come for the children's monsters.

Fairy love

Gra na griwog

Bless them, God may mind them, a light on them, touch the
mark, blind the eye, may they be kept, that old thing, this yoke,
ah not much, a silly little thing, tell it to the ditch . . .

I grew up with these apotropaic statements. They were
spoken to diminish the eye of jealousy and show you don't
take good fortune for granted. They were used to divert the
attention of the gentry, the elders of the hill, the Sí, the
griwog from that which might be considered precious, be it
a person, a cherished object, a relationship or a celebration.

In life we are rarely conscious of the old, whose
echoes resonate with us. These echoes become retellings of
retellings, each one a unique version of the story to hold
and then be recast. Amongst those tales are often, and more
than most realise, the tales of the griwog and their ancient
power and modern rumblings. For us the griwog are a
community of spirits of different origins. Among them are
thought to be fallen angels, the souls of ancestors, or the
living embodiment of nature.

Ask most these days if they believe in the griwog and
the answer is mostly no. But ask the same people would
they harm the blackthorn, the fort and rath, or disturb the
pathway of the horde and the answer, more often than not,
would also be no.

I learned this tale some summers ago as I sat in the
kitchen of an elder whose age was kept tucked away like a
secret coin, although many speculated about it. She told the
tale after a compliment about her home, so neatly kept and

warmed by the fire that crackled in the stove and the people who filled it. A warm remark is welcomed, but always end it with a blessing, or it might draw the attention of someone not seen at the table.

ohn was tall and broad, his wide shoulders proof of his life working from farm to farm. He had deep-brown eyes, the colour of the well-worn soil he worked with earnestness, and a pluck of dark hair with streaks of sun-kissed blond. His voice when he spoke sounded like he was about to sing. He was from a large family, his father being the seventh son and he the seventh of the seventh. Legend holds and people remember that these rare children are always gifted something from the otherworld and that those of the otherworld will always hold a longing for them.

He was only three days old when his father, having taken a shovel to the earth along the roadside, took from the upturned mud a worm and laid it into the small palm of the baby John. Rather than recoiling from the infant's grasp, the worm curled up tight and round. This was a sign, the father and his brothers remarked to one another, that meant that John, in time, would have the gift of a healer and the sight of a seer, someone with a foot planted firmly in one world but whose other shoe would graze often the land of the other. They knew too that the griwog might want him as much as his doting parents did, for it is a rare gift to exist in two realms, and this is a power longed for by the Sí, who are mostly restricted to only one land. They worried about him in all the usual ways but had the added concern that his life and being might draw the attention and affection of the griwog. But as the years passed and he grew safely into boyhood, much of this anxiety abated.

John was only a schoolboy when he first met Catherine, a neighbour's daughter, the child of a doctor. His brothers would joke on the way to school that they would be a good match, he a healer to be and she a child who grew up in the home of a physician. She had a bonny temperament, a strong will and a bright path ahead of her, one that nobody doubted she would forge for herself. She was known for her beauty. Her deep-green eyes were the colour of fresh uncurled ferns in spring, and her long mane of chestnut ringlets spilled over her shoulders to her hips. She was rarely alone, for people would naturally befriend her and find great solace and comfort in her company.

They lived in two worlds in a way. She of the buffer and he of the Mincéirí, but their glances often caught as they moved past each other, and while it was many years before a word was ever traded between them, their smiles, soft glimpses and the fresh flushing of their cheeks on sight of one another became the language of the young love between them.

Over time their subtle glances developed to cordial comments on the weather and local news. Before long they were chirping like two spring doves. On Sundays, after Mass, John would walk Catherine home. Their conversations moved from the recent homily to future adventures, of favourite songs sung and of their shared love of painting. A fistful of years came and went and each stayed faithful to the weekly walk, the sprawling conversation and the unspoken growing expectation of a proposal.

When John was eighteen and of age, he visited Catherine's home to start a conversation with her father about joining her family. He had made no declaration to Catherine and thought it best to seek approval, as was the way of the time. He was hopeful as their weekly walk was not a secret and, although not spoken of, was never opposed.

Catherine's father, a decent man, met John on the porch of their home and asked him why he was there. When John answered, a half-smile crept across the father's lips and he replied that the only person to be asked was Catherine herself.

The next week, on their track towards her home from mass, John proposed with a ring he himself had worked from a silver pound coin, and in delight Catherine loudly exclaimed a yes. Soon the village was aclatter with the noise of their good news.

After the proposal came the meeting of their people.

John's family were greeted with a warm welcome at Catherine's home, where no one was surprised to be meeting each other. As the parents sat across the table, questions and inquiries poured out before them, like hail falling from a winter's sky, and Catherine smiled.

John's mother, having grown comfortable, asked for a fresh cup of weéd and Catherine, puzzled, said they only had tea. As the family chuckled, John explained that weéd was a word amongst their people for the very thing.

'A silly thing for me to say,' spluttered Catherine as she shifted in her seat out of embarrassment.

'Far from it,' whispered John as he looked lovingly at her. 'Nothing but a goodness could come from that sweet mouth of yours.'

When the evening was drawing to a close, John and his family rose to leave. On their way John grasped Catherine's hand, tightly squeezing it and telling her how much he looked forward to sharing their future together. They were oblivious to the narrowed eyes and twitching ears of the griwog, who were lurking behind the hawthorns, crouched by elder bushes, wrapped sinuously around the trunks of alders and perched high on the branches of silver birch.

Next morning when Catherine awoke, she felt a pain creep across her face and linger along her jaws. It was a dull gnaw, as if she had being chewing for too long on early-autumn apples. As she traced her tongue along the inside of her mouth, she discovered to her horror a mound of flesh, softened at the tip and drawing downwards. She quickly wrapped her lips inwards and they receded further than they had ever before. A panicked scramble to the bathroom mirror brought with it the terrible discovery. She had no teeth. None at all. Each one was gone. Her inner jawline was flat and fresh, like she never had the milk teeth of infancy or the back molars that came with sense and age. A terrible thing. A frightful learning.

Word spread quickly of the happening and soon came the rumour as to why. It was the griwogs, the neighbours said. John, a man of two worlds, held the keen interest of those of the hills. What the gentry wanted, they would often want to keep to themselves, and Catherine's calamity was a warning. He, the seventh son of the seventh son, was marked as theirs.

As soon as John heard, he raced to her side and tried to put silence to such thoughts, inviting her and her kin to his family's fireside. Time spent with them in the molly, her a warmly welcomed bride-to-be would, he thought, banish any such superstition of his life not being his to share.

Catherine's father, being a man of medicine, searched books and thick tomes of research, and assured his daughter that such a thing was hardly heard of, and it being so rare, would be best ignored. To linger on it brought nothing but an invitation for more worry.

The evening at the molly was a great success. Conversation flowed as freely as the river beside them – a return of her family's welcome with so much warmth and affection that the couple knew more than ever that they were a good match.

Still, Catherine worried about the rumours and the awkwardness of her new appearance. She held her hand in front of her face as she spoke. John, when he could, delicately reminded her that their love was above such surface things. As the night drew in, they hugged each other in a departing embrace. John gently brushed her glossy curls behind her ears and, kissing his hand, placed on top of her head a loving blessing until they would see each other again.

The next morning Catherine awoke colder than usual and sat up among her thick blankets of cotton and pillows of feather-stuffed wool. Shaking the sleep from her, she noticed how light her head felt. She went to comb her fingers through her hair but her hands were met with only the soft roundness of her head.

Her hair was gone.

It had not fallen out, for not a single strand of her locks could be found on, in or under her bed. Even the comb with which she had brushed it only a few hours before was empty, neither réb nor strand clinging to it.

Crying in the kitchen, Catherine threw off the wedding, saying it was a sign too many to be ignored and that she would have no more of it, despite her heart's loud call for John. John, defiant to any notion that the griwog had a claim to him, and his love as strong and enduring, begged her to reconsider, assuring her that her appearance did not matter. As they talked of their plans and the shared kindling between them, Catherine warmed to the renewed idea of marriage. John spoke of his hopes for them both and said that if she was patient with him, one day her beautiful eyes might see him, too, bald and toothless.

The families decided to quicken the road to the wedding and have done by it. The next Sunday, their usual walking day, would be the day they walked down the aisle.

On the nights coming up to the wedding, Catherine's family gathered about her, promising to stand in watch at the foot of her bed to ensure that no malice would befall her. Her bridesmaids, three in total, all decided that they would wear matching clothing, with red scarfs at night across their faces and concealing the manes of their heads. They stitched dresses of simple linen in hopes that in dressing the same, in looking the same, whatever force was menacingly tormenting her would be confused and drawn away from her as a victim.

Catherine barely slept. Her nights were filled with the heavy chains and shackles of worry and fear, that kept dreams a stranger from her mind. On the morning of the wedding, she was met with the cheerfulness of her bridesmaids, who presented her with her new garment, which they had all shared in the making of, and with words of hope that a beautiful day was ahead of them all and, most of all, ahead of her and her beloved.

The miserable days behind her seemed to drop away as the bridesmaids and the bride began the morning preparations. They placed flowers upon their heads, montbretia, celandine and red campion, shared a breakfast of cheese and milk and laid out seeds for the birds to nibble on, hoping to draw upon themselves as much good luck as they could.

Catherine, whose heart was now all the happier, decided to have a quick nap before her carriage arrived, to offset the long trek towards the day and, while determined to meet each moment with vigour and celebration, could not dismiss the toll of what had happened to her. The bridesmaids distracted with their duties and the family busy with the greeting and welcome of extended kin and neighbours, left her to sleep upon her bed, promising to rustle her from her rest before the carriage arrived. She sighed a sound of delighted contentment before unwinding herself to slumber.

She awoke to darkness.

She thought that the curtains must be too tightly closed, but as she stretched and yawned upon her bed, the realisation slowly began to rise in her. She moved her hands slowly along her face, catching first at the chin and then her lips, stiff and thin in the horror of the moment, gliding upwards to her nose and the wetness of her cheeks that were dripping in her tears. She rounded the lids of her eyes to press down softly on the orbs and found that they were not there. A piercing scream was heard through the home that has long since echoed in the stones and very foundation of the building.

Her bed was empty when the bridesmaids made their way to it. That night she was reclaimed from the river, still in her bridal dress.

When they laid her out at home, on the same table at which she and John had exchanged smiles and warmth, she was returned to who she was. Her teeth, hair and eyes were intact, as if they had never been touched. The only thing now missing was the glow of life in her, as she lay there pale and rigid, breathless and lifeless, lost to all those who had loved her.

John never married. His heart never again sought out love. Instead he filled his days and evenings studying the ways and works of the griwogs and became known as a fairy doctor. He had paid the heaviest of prices for his knowledge. That lesson is even now passed down through the generations, warning those who speak that not everyone present may be seen.

Bless you.

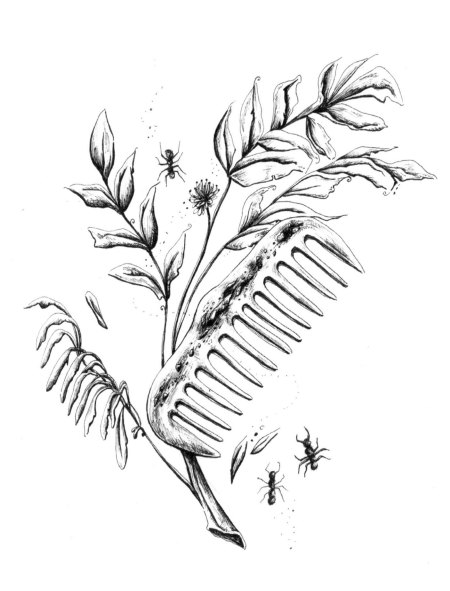

The comb
A rirk

Life often has many unspoken rules, ways of courtesy and respect that we learn through reflection and observance, by seeing the world about us and figuring out how to navigate it. Alongside the unspoken rules are those that are very directly named, announced, shared and not considered an option. Some rules are bent or stretched and broken; some, however, are kept pristine like newly minted pennies.

The convention of avoiding a strange unowned comb is by many Mincéirí, especially the older generation, earnestly followed. These combs are believed to belong to griwog-beoirs, who are sometimes seen grooming their locks by the riverside. Our lore is full of tales of these fairy women who cry the lamentations that foretell a passing, who are graceful to lost wanderers and who extend the most brutal of punishments to those who would take from them.

There is a road not far from my family home that is rarely travelled. It's a thin, winding boreen that rolls and rambles through the countryside, passing under the tall arms of ash trees, down to a clear patch of short grass and moss that is flanked by three grey slabs of stone, which crown a sacred well.

Around the time of my birth, the well was filled in by local council workers to claim back the space for a new road network, one that had not been formally passed as a plan by the town assembly. That same night eerie wails and screams began to roll out from the well, stretching across the surrounding land. The story was covered by a regional newspaper, the article attributing the clamour to disturbed animals in the area who had used the well as a place to quench their thirst. But the well was not the only point of water in that grove in the west of wet Connaught. The neighbours, the locals, those who lived within an ear's hearing of it all, spoke in hushed tones and sometimes in voices lifted high in anger of the screams that were heard at night. Within a week, the silt and stone, gravel and rocks that had been poured into the well were dug out and a fresh boundary was established about it.

That place not only marks the ground of that tale but of another story of two sisters, a mischief and a comb.

Theresa and Biddy were twins. Well, that's what they called each other, having been born in the same year. Theresa took her first breath on the first Sunday after Christmas and Biddy during the full moon at the time of Samhain. In this older community, time was counted differently than today, as not everyone had a calendar on a wall or the company of a ticking wristwatch. Instead the dates and moving of nature were the markers. Time was defined by the movement of the seasons, the rites of Mass and the gathering at festivals and markets.

Theresa was tall, with a fashion of wearing flowers in her hair. As she and her family moved from molly to molly, she would take the small pebbles she found in her boot and carry them as little worry stones in her beady pocket close to her hip. When in a brood, she would pour all her heart's fears into them, but when they felt heavier in her grasp, she would flick them from her hand at a crossroad. There are many directions to travel from a crossroad and so stones cast off would hopefully not find her again.

Biddy, when standing on her stretched toes, hovered at shoulder height to her sister. She was loud, but not in voice, as she would often get caught in the briars of shyness when in the company of those outside of her family. Rather she was a child who could hardly cross a road without causing a commotion. Jugs carried rarely went unspilled, a watched fire was not safe from going out under her attention, and her parents knew that if ever a message needed to be quickly sent, they could tell it to Biddy as a secret and trust that within a day word of it would probably get to the Pope himself.

Biddy and Theresa adored each other, sharing secrets and dreams, whispers and notions, and for the time of their youth, they were the closest of friends and confidantes. They were close and, like a shoe and a sock, were almost always together.

One morning in the height of summer as the sun pierced the sky and the tufts of grass along the roadside grew brown and dry in the presence of that solar fire, their parents decided that the labour in the area that they had called their home for a toss of days had come to its own natural conclusion. They planned that they should move westerly, towards a larger town with more prospect of work.

The family were not alone, for there was a chain of their kin linking their way through the area, taking refuge in the shelter of trees, the tender turns of the road and the hospitality of an open common field.

The moving day was a busy one. The carts were filled, with the few family possessions heaped up high upon it. The wheels of the wagon checked and rounded, the horses fed and stall-watered, the fires quenched and the rings of stones about them returned to their fields, and the ashes either buried or laid out as a way-shower for those who might follow after them.

The father of the twins understood that the best spots for a fresh molly, those of silence and coverage away from the pathways of man, living or dead, and the track routes of ants, would be in great demand. Knowing the long road before them and the many people behind them also searching for a new haven, he sent Theresa and Biddy on ahead to cross the land and fields to the sacred well he recalled from previous travels. And they had always found a safe home there under the protection of the griwog-beoir who resided there, never seen but whose benign presence could be felt. It was a coveted spot, as there was quick access to water on it as well as shelter from ash trees. The site was open enough to be in solid view, but set back away from the trodden path, so the molly would not intrude on the labour of the local farmers, and they would be able to see anyone who approached the camp.

The sisters leaped over mounds and walls, glided through fields and pastures, taking the distance in their stride. Youth and the want of a safe space fuelled them mightily.

When they arrived at the well, they found it a sombre place. Hardly a flower was in bloom or a bird perched with songs in its throat upon any local tree. They blamed the summer. With the height of the sun, sure it was no surprise to them that the land and the feathered flock might be taking a rest, and so they sat waiting for their family to follow them.

As they gazed off out onto the horizon, with its speckles of trees and slowly descending sun, they saw a storm crawling towards them, growing in shades of grey. First came a light drizzle that brought with it a kiss of relief, but soon they found themselves awash with rain, a steady deluge that made deep puddles about them.

The sisters took some shelter under the branches of the trees, rubbing their arms at the sudden loss of heat. The wind grew uneasy, moaning and groaning its distaste in a heavy breath upon them. The twins, too, began to sigh and share in the weariness of the wind and rain. As they stood there, wet to the bone, cold to the core and miserable of spirit, they began to speak of turning back along the road that they had travelled, to the company of their family.

Before leaving, Biddy declared that their parents might be disappointed that they would be giving up the best resting place, and together they hatched a plan. Going through Theresa's beady pocket, they found her comb, and, sharing a glance, they thrust the comb into a rising along the ground.

Theresa turned to her sister with a wide-lipped grin. 'This,' she stated with an air of confidence, 'will keep the spot for us.' She made sure to tear up in brisk handfuls the grass that grew around so the comb would be easily seen.

As they turned to leave, Theresa fell back onto the ground and landed with a thick whump on the wet lawn of grass. Startled at first, she saw that it was her dress snagged on a branch of the tree which threw her off her balance. As she lay there wrestling back her sense of calm, she felt a hand tugging at her foot, drawing her not along the ground closer to the tree but downwards into the very soil on which she was scrambling to regain a foothold. She could feel the bite of the cold, damp claw, unyielding in its grip, unrelenting in its want to drag her beneath. The earth began to sink under her, the draw of the hand ever-stronger. It was as if the ground was becoming water and she would soon find herself beneath waves of sod.

She called out with arms outstretched to her sister, but

Biddy did not answer, for she was distracted by the sound of the tree itself. Through the rustle of the tree's movement in the wind and the loud patter of rain on its branches, Biddy had heard a voice call out, asking her to stay.

Theresa summoned her strength for her bewitched sister. With a sharp roar, she wrenched free and crawled frantically away from the tree. Jumping to her feet and taking Biddy's hand, she made a swift retreat back to the safety of the road. Once they had a firmer footing, Theresa shook Biddy by the shoulders, calling out the prayers of her people, and jostled her back to the world.

Although they took quick gallop and wide strides, the journey to their family seemed a longer one, and the road stretched on and turned where it had never before. It was holding them back, keeping them close to the field with the well. Soon the sun, which had been long descending, set and the warm glow of orange and red was no longer, and all they had was the warmth and sight of each other.

In time the families were spotted along the road, moving like ants in a procession. As soon as they were in earshot, the two sisters began, while still catching their breath, to share their tale of the sudden change in weather, the whisperings of the trees and the phantom hand that laid its cold hold on Theresa's foot. A shudder rippled out amongst the families, more so among the elders for whom the griwog remain a living fear. The younger people, not so convinced of the intrusion of the otherworld, placated the girls but kept steady in their stride. When Biddy shared with them her craftiness with the comb, her father decided to continue the journey and claim the best spot.

Biddy's grandmother, however, who sat at the back of the cart, her legs swaying with every bump and bash of the road, scolded her.

'There's no need to worry the good lady,' she said sternly at the thought of the sisters' actions. 'It's all well and good wanting a spot and working towards it, but you can't cheat for it and stir up the good people. Not only is there folly in it, there's a danger.'

She urged her son to turn the reins and find another sheltering spot, as the best spot, without safety, would be of no comfort.

The father of the twins laughed kindly but offered no reply, and casting his glance aside, thought how old-fashioned such a worry was. Not wanting to upset his mother, he continued to walk alongside the cart in silence, while she sat scrunching her face in trepidation as they took the long road back to the well.

As they drew near, the horses that pulled their carts and wagons would not go any closer. Their nostrils flared out with fear as their tails whipped back and forth. They stood apprehensively on the road, their hooves clicking loudly against the stone as if they were preparing to race.

The sisters, having lost their fear in the company of family, approached, planning to reclaim the comb, exclaiming delightedly at having stolen away the spot. As they reached down, they discovered that the comb that they had left was not the one standing there, handle first from the soil. Instead of the plain comb with its fawn wood and simple teeth, there was a comb of shining silver encrusted with emeralds and rubies, a spine of gold from the tip to the hilt. The sisters stopped short, with eyes fixed on it. As the breeze passed through the fine teeth of the comb, there was a hum like a melody, luring them closer to claim it. And their parents began to drift closer to the comb too.

It was only their grandmother's voice, grainy with age, calling from the cart, that drew the family back to the road, breaking the hold of the griwog tune. Shaken by the realisation of the danger they had been in, the family and their kin left that day and none again stayed by the well. And neither did any of those wanderers take to cheating to claim any spot.

Whispers

Leskoi

Names have power in ways I think we are only beginning to understand. When we're born, we have a sound assigned to us, a name, and over time that sound is used to invoke us; it embodies us. With time and use our names are stitched into us and into our relationships with one another. As a child I was fascinated by names, their origins and meanings, and the reasons why people were named as they are.

Many Mincéirí live in a space of multiple names. We have our legal names on our birth certs, we have our family titles and then we have nicknames. Together these names give a place to us in history and connection and very often emerge from a deep thread of humour. In our names we are gathered up and welcomed in, but what happens, you might wonder, when your name is not just for calling but for drawing out . . . and not always for the betterment?

There are many versions of this tale. It has grown and spread through veins and vines over the years to include other encounters that are woven into the spaces between the known and unknowable. It was originally gifted to me by Mary Reilly, who in my youth I knew and adored as Pink Mary for her love of the bright colour and because her own mother was named Rosey. Mary was and will always be one of my closest childhood friends, and this tale, when shared with me, was about trust, awareness and a question: who knows us as who we really are rather than who they think we are?

Pink Mary told me this story in the front garden of

her home in Tirboy, a well-kept lawn lined with bursts of flowers, where pine trees towered over us, and in which two wonderful chubby-legged dogs made their presence known with a bark or a little lick at the hand and a wiggle of their stubby tails.

Names can be an escape or a prison. Sometimes they are the sign of a trap.

There was once a family who lived along the south-western shore of Ireland. They lived a life of small comforts and a high heap of love. There was the grandmother, Kitty, her daughter, Mary, and her granddaughters, Kathleen and Eileen. There were no men in their home, for some years earlier, while the grandfather and Mary's husband were fishing for food for their table, a great swell had risen up and swallowed them whole. They were kept by the sea in her relentless grasp, and neither body, boat nor oar were ever seen again.

The children were young when the men were claimed by the waves, and what few memories they had of their father and grandfather faded like marks on the beach as another tide, that of time, rolled on in their lives. The loss of grandfather and father was a great scar upon the family, a wound that would never quite heal. Kitty and Mary rarely spoke to the children about the loss, for fear that treading heavily on their memories would only leave footprints of grief. Rarely, too, did they venture close to large bodies of water, the memory being too raw and the sight of it too close to the sorrow that moved in its own rhythms within them.

By the time Kathleen, who was older than her sister by a year, was eight, her mother and grandmother never spoke of the lost men at all. It was a space carved in pain. Silence had developed in their lives and, unknown to them, this was not only a loss but a risk. For all the protections in the world, knowing of a pure, simple love and of those who have loved you is as mighty as the raised blade of battlefield angels.

One night, Kathleen was wrapped up tight in bed in a room she shared with her little sister, Eileen, in a cocoon of blankets her mother had wrapped them in to keep the winter's bite at bay. She wore a bright-red hat with fraying threads along the rim, which almost matched the flame colour of her hair, and thick woolly socks on her feet, bathing her in a snug warmth that was just as comforting as her mother's embrace. Her little nose was all that really felt the cold as she sniffled the frosty air about her and tried to drift off to sleep in hopes of a morning of softer weather.

Eileen was deep in the wanderings of dreams as Kathleen lay there watching the curtains swaying slowly back and forth in the draft, as if in sync with her sister's breathing. As she herself began to meander and the senses of the world stepped back, the sound of the wind outside began to mix with the sound of Eileen's snoring.

Suddenly Kathleen was jolted back from her sleepy daze by a tapping on the window. It was not the gentle pitter-patter of the rain as it swept through the garden, but a series of sharp knocks against the pane. With the bravery of youth, she uncoiled herself from the blankets, rose from the bed and threw open the curtains to see what had caused such a thing. But only the heavy rain-bearing clouds grumbled overhead.

It must have been a twig, she thought, tossed through the air by the wind, and with a cautious hand, so as not to disturb her sister, she drew the curtains and returned to her bed.

'Come outside, for I have the most exciting things to show you,' the familiar voice of her mother chimed. Kathleen sat upright. At first the clarity of the words was such that it seemed as if the voice was in the room with her, but no one stood close to her bedside.

'Come, my child, for we don't have long,' coaxed the voice.

Kathleen, jumped from her bed. It seemed as if her mother was calling her from outside. She moved closer to the window, her breath clouding the glass.

'Come, my child, hurry.'

The sound of her mother's voice was alluring and safe, a siren's song for the child. The voice poured over her, urging her outside. She slowly opened the sash window and reached out, fingers spread wide and searching into the darkness for her mother's grasp. Her hand met only the bitter chill of night air. Kathleen peeked out the window but all she could see was the stark cold blackness of the night and the heavy clouds that hung menacingly above her home.

The young girl, in her confusion, called out to her mother, her beseeching voice reaching out across the lawn to the sentinel-like trees that stood along the boundary of her home. No reply came. Kathleen climbed out of the open window and landed with a heavy thud on the moist ground. Crying out for her mother, the young girl stumbled through the garden but could not see her. Instead she was met with the darkness of the night and an ashen fog that wrapped itself around her.

She heard her mother's voice, more urgent this time, but it sounded further away. She wandered through the fog but could hardly see. It was as if the fog itself was a blindfold upon her face and she could only now and again catch glimpses of her surroundings.

As she continued to follow the voice, which called out to her in growing desperation, the cold and the dampness of the night began to wear on Kathleen and she began to consider a return home. Every so often the fog would thin and her eyes would catch sight of the thickness of the trees but also the light of her home, there on the horizon like a lighthouse in a storm. Kathleen soon realised that no matter how closely she followed the sound of the voice, she couldn't reach her mother. She grew unsure and then unwilling to follow it.

She traced her way back home, watching the light shining from a window as her guide, stopping now and again to catch her breath and regain her footing.

On scampering back in through the window, she fell as her numb toes caught the edge of the curtains, pulling them with her as she fell with a thud to the floor. The commotion woke her sister, who let out a loud short scream. Her mother rushed to the room and stood there for a moment in surprise to see her daughter, cold and dripping wet from the rain of the night, in a bundle upon on the floor.

When Kathleen told her mother that she had been following her voice, her mother dismissed it without a moment's thought and guided her daughter to the hot press for a fresh nightgown and a warm towel for her hair.

'Sleepwalking,' Mary said, 'sleep walking and wandering. You must have gotten a dream in your head and started to follow it.'

The next morning, with the night before hardly a memory, Kathleen spoke to all those who sat about the breakfast table of her dream adventures out into the wild. If it was not for the muddy bedclothes waiting to be washed and her memory of the bitter gnawing of the cold upon her, especially her toes, it would have passed from her mind into the great forgotten. As Kathleen spoke in a cheerful manner of her night, as if imparting a joke, Kitty, her grandmother, sat silently listening, spinning her wedding ring anxiously on her finger, her gaze firmly on Kathleen, her mouth opening wider and wider in horror.

Blessing herself, the old woman interrupted her granddaughter and told them of the stoka gresko, the whisperer, a being never seen who could take on the voices of the ones you trust the most. It had a vicious hunger for the pain of its victims, a ferocious thirst for the tears of those it did harm to and a want most of all for the last breath of those it had tricked to their demise. The one thing it could not do, was say the name of those it stalked. Words of endearment were its crafty tools. A kind tone concealed its darksome intent, and familiarity with the sound of that voice was a trusted key that unlocked the barred doors of many a home. It liked children most of all, for the fear of children is purest, and the fires of their imaginations are well stocked and easily stoked. The young are quick to trust and are brave enough to venture where many older would never go.

The children giggled at the story as they ate their porridge, their minds resting more on the day ahead of them rather than Kathleen's adventure the night before.

That evening the mother laid a damp cloth at the window in Kathleen's bedroom in the hope that its touch would wake Kathleen if she were to climb through it. As the mother tucked her daughters into bed with words of warmth and blessings, they whispered each other's names as the night and the stillness of sleep wrapped about them. As a fresh morning broke, the thoughts of the stoka gresko, the whisperer, had passed and were as fleeting as the memory of their dreams.

Mary had decided she would visit a friend she had not seen for some time, and her daughters were just as excited to go, for her friend had a sprawling home on the edge of a hill by a lake, surrounded by thick-barked trees, one of which had a swing on it made from the blue nylon rope from a local farm and an old car tyre. As they walked the long, winding road towards the home, Eileen, being spring-footed and of high energy, rushed ahead towards the tree with the swing, and Kathleen and her mother lost view of her. When the path split between the route towards the tree and that of the home of their friend, Mary stood as she watched Kathleen run up to the tree. Kathleen called back to Mary that Eileen was sitting on a branch among the leaves.

Mary was greeted with a great warmth by her friend, who ushered her into the kitchen, a room lined with tall cabinets, with a round dark-wood table in its centre, standing on a mossy green rug. A pot was boiling upon the fire, and soon Mary was sipping tea as she leaned against the sink in the kitchen, keeping a soft eye out the window on Kathleen swinging on the car tyre. Kathleen's head was tilted upwards and she was talking and giggling.

Her friend, recognising the long walk from her home, invited Mary to sit in the living room, where the sofa, with its plush cushions, would provide more relief than the hard oak chairs of the kitchen. As soon as Mary entered the room, she let out a loud gasp, for there in the corner sat Eileen, nose deep in a book. In bewilderment she asked how she had gotten from the tree to the chair so quickly. Little Eileen and the hostess answered in confusion that she had been ensconced there all along. Alarm rose in Mary. She rushed to the kitchen window and saw to her dread that the swing on which Kathleen had been spinning only a few moments ago was now empty and swaying like an ominous pendulum.

Mary opened the back door with such force that the very hinges of it were almost torn from the frame. She passed the threshold, raced across the garden to the base of the tree. A scream rose in her throat. 'Kathleen!'

Her cries were piercing as she paced about, searching every space she could see. Her friend, on making her way to Mary, drew them back into the moment, away from panic and the worry. 'She can't have gone far. I'll head to the wood and you go round the lake. We'll find her. We'll find her.'

Mary needed no further discussion. She raced along the lake line, half tempted to dive in, if not for the memories of her father and husband lost. As she made her way along the lake, she spotted Kathleen's red hair, a flag amongst the green, and while the muscles of her legs burned and her breathing was laboured, she bounded towards her, leaping over fallen branches and stones.

Kathleen was waist deep in the water of the lake. Mary,

neither thinking nor pausing but alive with the impulse of a mother, jumped into the water. A spray of foam rose from about her limbs as she strode deeper into the lake, closer and closer to Kathleen. She reached out and grabbed the collar of Kathleen's dress and dragged her backwards, out of the water up onto the embankment.

As soon as Kathleen was safe in her arms, Mary began scolding her, but each word was punctuated with a relieved kiss upon her head.

She was safe. For now.

From that day forward, and there thankfully were many days that came afterwards, none amongst her people, or her people's people, would ever reply to a call that did not carry with it their name. Kathleen heard the call often, of course, at night, at dawn, sometimes while she was distracted or lost in a thought.

The whisperer, once it has taken a liking to someone, rarely leaves them until they are beneath the sacred soil or across the great waters over which it rarely travels. Kathleen was never again fooled by it, but neither was she ever left alone by those who loved her, for they knew it waited, patient as the stones that become the mountains. In time she gave her own children a secret name, whispered into their ears at birth and kept deep in the folds of her own heart, for if those secret names, their true names, were never known, then they could never be touched by the stoka gresko.

The boggy boots

An ladu guillimers

One of the bogs we worked on was called the backfield. It lay behind the high mound of the Sandhill, where the Athenry Road met the lane to Cloontooa. Of all the bogs on which my hands have turned the sods, this one was the kindest. The peat was firm and quick to dry and there was a line of furze bushes that trailed up and down the field, blocking the cut of any winds. The air would be filled with the scents of the rising summer from those furze bushes, along with the deep, sweet fragrance of coconut gorse.

I was a boy who had perfected the art of distraction. The turning of turf wasn't a deeply laborious task for my young body. It was far more trying thing for my spirit; it was monotonous. Every powder-blue moth and silver-winged dragonfly seemed to invite me to follow it. I found myself, more than once, sliding down the loose ditch of a bog hole. I never quite fell into those murky waters, always managing to find some foothold. But on one occasion, I wasn't able to climb back out and spent, what felt to my youthful heart, a lifetime calling for aid, trying to out-roar the noise from the car radio, which was left playing loudly, car doors wide open, to entertain us all as we worked.

I was dragged from the ditch and patted down to ensure I was intact, but there was no pity for me. They had a good sense of me, and while they had been labouring hard, I had been complaining harder. I had survived yet another misadventure, and as the day was trailing on, my Uncle Davie, who moved through the lines of sod like he was wading water rather than mud, told me this tale of that very bog, and he who was within it.

Once there was a home that stood tall and proud in the middle of a field not far from the bog. It was a simple house, with slate roof tiles and whitewashed walls. The fire in its hearth had warmed many neighbours and the larders were rarely bare. The melodies of generations hummed in the panes of the windows and the wooden chairs at the dinner table were worn smooth from the coming and going of friends.

The home was owned by two siblings, Irish twins born eleven months apart, the eldest a woman, the younger a man, and they kept it in good care. The woman was named Ciara, for when she was born she had locks of pitch-black hair longer than herself, which her mother would wrap around her like a blanket. She was soft and naïve and remained so into adulthood, and no cynical seed that fell around her ever took root. Her younger brother was named Michael for the archangel because of a birthmark in the shape of a sword on his upper arm. Mick embodied his name with his protective nature and enduring grace.

As Ciara reached womanhood, she decided to find herself a husband, and in little time she married a man from Mayo, who was known as Grade, for he loved money but was loathe to share it. For all his irascibility with others, when it came to Ciara, Grade was honey-mouthed, with sweet words that drew her in. She thought him a man of humour with a sharp wit, and in the kindness of her own heart, believed his harsh comments to others were light bristles to provoke thought, rather than the deep thorns that they were.

Grade knowing the treasure he had found in the innocent Ciara and, wanting both her presence and her homestead, kept his true face from her, allowing her to live the dream as he lived the lie.

To most others, Grade and Ciara were an odd match, like a horse in a dress, but for some time they lived happily and continued to share the home with her brother. Mick never took to Grade and could see clearly the man he was but, loving Ciara dearly, would never interfere on any path she herself chose to take. He remained in their home and kept watch.

As the years stretched, Grade began to sour, knowing the land and house and all that it contained would go to the eldest son, Mick. This knowledge pressed heavily on his mind. In his pride, he did not like the feeling that he was living in a home with his wife by the pleasure and agreement of her brother and not his own will. This of course led to arguments between Grade and Mick, nights of shouting and days of silence. Mick had little care for who owned the house and the lands, for Ciara was his sister and it was her home, and he had no intention of parting with either of them.

One night, while Ciara visited some friends who rarely had time or talk for Grade, he and Mick sat beside the open fire. With the topic of the ownership of the home dancing across the main stage of Grade's mind, he asked Mick to sign over the place to him. Mick would have a room there, of course, for as long as he wanted. Mick shook his head, for if all three were safe and welcome to stay in their home, then there was no reason to change the deeds.

Grade bubbled and stewed in silence, and when Mick rose from his chair to throw a few extra sods upon the flame, Grade snuck up behind him, and with the blunt of a kamog, he struck Mick down. The force of the blow was such that Mick was unable to rise again. As he dropped, the only sound to be heard was the thud of his limp body crashing against the floor. Immediately a bone-deep dread moved through Grade, a downpour of horror in which the fire of his rage was washed away. His eyes were wide in alarm, the kamog dropped from his trembling, guilty hand. Panic rose in him, not for the slaying of his brother-in-law, but in the realisation that Ciara would soon be home.

Taking Mick's body by both of its still-warm hands, Grade dragged it through grit and gravel, over grass and grain to the edge of the bog and rolled it into a bog hole. The waters bubbled loudly as the body sank, sucked down beneath its murky water. Grade watched it disappear from his view, smirking, until the last of the ripples was gone.

The next morning, as the sun rose, Ciara noticed her brother's absence at the breakfast table and knocked loudly on his bedroom door. Hearing no reply, and anxious, she peeped inside. The bed was empty, neat and tidy, made in full, and clearly had not been slept upon. Grade, on hearing this, threw up a fog of excuses. Maybe he went out to a pub and was distracted and would be back later. Maybe he was unwell and left to see a doctor and they would find him happy and on the mend in a hospital bed. Maybe he was sick of them and had gathered himself up in a moment and left the house to them.

None of these suggestions found fertile ground in Ciara's imagination. She knew her brother would not leave their home without a farewell and that the village was small enough that any ill tidings of health or misadventure would have travelled to her quickly. By the time the noon Angelus bell had rung, she had reported her brother missing. The police took heed at first but soon tired in their investigations. They knew of no one against him. He had no shady past, nor had he wandered paths that led him to or from trouble, and largely he was a man well-known and liked.

As time passed and Mick remained missing, it became a mystery that locals spoke of and the young made whispers of, with rumours of men from the north stealing him away, and of the calls of the griwogs binding him under the many local raths. None thought that Grade was at fault, and he wore the guise and garments of loss well. His sneaky smile rarely danced across his face, and he let his wife's tear-stained face rest on his shoulder as he consoled her. Mick's disappearance remained a mystery to all but Grade, who knew that his brother-in-law had been left fouled in a cold, damp bog hole.

Ciara kept Mick's room as it was, never turning a cushion or shaking a single coat in his wardrobe. It became a dust-filled and spider-web-woven altar to his life until one morning, after five long years of missing him, Ciara decided that wherever he was, he would not be making his road back to her. As the sunlight crept along the horizon, she rose from her bed and began to gather up his belongings. She took his shirts, his ties and hats, jumpers and cuffs, shoes and boots, everything she thought could find a new life with someone else, and made her way to the local charity shop and offered them up in return for consolation for her heart and an unspoken prayer in his remembrance.

Johnny, a Mincéir man from Mayo, who wore a hat of crimson with a horseshoe nail-pinned along its brim and a long brown tweed coat that had seen better days, was travelling through town and happened upon the very same charity shop that Ciara had visited a few days earlier. In it, he found a pair of boots, light caramel in tone and just the right size. He liked to wiggle his toes while he walked, and the boots he had found were nice and wide, a rare find. The shopkeeper asked for a shilling. No haggle from Johnny, who thought it a fair exchange, never knowing that they had belonged to Ciara's brother nor of the unexpected journey he was about to take.

That night as Johnny prepared himself for bed, he checked on his children, left the boots wrapped in burlap beside his bed, and welcomed a much-needed sleep beside his slumbering wife.

The next morning he woke to an unexpected sight. He did not see the inner canvas of his loban, nor the smiling face of his wife waking for the day, but found himself instead standing, fully dressed, with the boots upon his feet, outside an unfamiliar home, the house of Ciara and Grade. Startled by the sharp snap back to consciousness, he was dazed for a few moments before he rested himself and releasing a sigh – part confusion, part humour. He took the road back to his camp and eagerly told them of his night-time sleepwalking, a sign, his wife said, of a busy mind that was wont to wander.

Days and nights passed, and while Johnny went to bed tired with a head filled with dreams, time and time again he would awake to find himself standing by the gable end of Grade and Ciara's home, perched up like a carrion crow on the dry-stone wall that marked the boundaries of their land. The nightly wanders to Grade and Ciara's home became so normal that soon Johnny, his wife and family rarely spoke of them. Each morning as Ciara drew back the curtain, she would see Johnny go down the road towards his molly. She never wondered why he was there. To her innocent eyes, he appeared to be a man going with intent about his business.

The season of winter began to sink away from the land, and Johnny once again felt the draw to travel the roads for fresh adventure, new employment and perhaps a night's rest. One day he was in town gathering the last of the supplies for the making of a journey east towards an upcoming festival, and while on his way back to his cart, the heels of his boots shook and shuddered before holding themselves still in the air, just before he was able to place a foot upon the ground. As he watched in surprise, his feet, moving of their own accord started to lunge towards Grade, who was leaving the local bank and making his way home. At first Grade didn't notice Johnny's approach, and his eyes were only eventually drawn to him by his exaggerated gestures.

Startled by Johnny's approach, Grade began to attack him, and they traded shout and clout as they grappled to the ground. As they fought, Grade recognised the boots on Johnny's feet as Mick's. A cold sliver of fear went through Grade's heart, somehow understanding that the boots were involved with the nightly visits and current ruckus. As they both struggled back to standing, Grade gave Johnny a sharp punch to his chest, knocking him again to the roadside. He swiftly pulled the boots from Johnny's feet and took off home before any more words could be said or blows exchanged. Johnny rose to his feet, bewildered and bruised in both body and pride, and returned to his molly barefoot.

That night, as Ciara slept, Grade retrieved the bewitched boots from where he had hidden them beneath the holly bush that grew beside a stile across the road. Entering the house quickly and checking that Ciara, his doting wife, was still asleep, he set the boots onto the red-hot coals of the hearth fire. As he watched, he was stunned to discover that the licks and flame tops of the fire curled away from the boots and they would not burn. He stood there for some time, turning the boots with the tongs, willing them to catch aflame, but the fire itself was denying Grade the chance to hide his guilt. Filling with anger, Grade grabbed the stone-cold boots from the fire by their lacers and they swung by his hips, intact and untouched by the fire. Knowing trouble would most certainly befall him if Ciara were to wake and find him in possession of her missing brother's boots, he decided, in a rush of desperation, to take the winding boreen to the bogside, where he flung them into a bog hole. He returned under the mantle of the dark night to his home and slipped softly into his bed.

He awoke in the early hours, his pillow wet from the sweating of his nightmares and his bedclothes tight around his body from tossing and turning in discomfort. As his eyes slowly adjusted to the light of the room, his senses were not drawn outwards but closer in, towards himself. He felt a tightness on his feet, with neither space for toe to wiggle nor ankle to flex. Thinking the blankets must have become entangled, he drew them back and saw, to his horror, that his feet were tightly encased in the mud-encrusted boots. They were dripping wet, a mash of mud oozing out over the rims, and their tongues lashed tight against his ankle, as if holding back their words.

He leaped from his bed and took sharp kicking steps towards the kitchen to try to shake the boots off. The boots, still soaked in filthy bog water, squelched on his feet, as if his decomposing victim was reaching out with gurgled taunts against him from his boggy grave. He rummaged through the cutlery until he found the sharpest of paring knives and struck at the boots with deep growls. But the blade simply rolled off the lacers like raindrops against slate, neither unweaving a thread nor making even the simplest of marks on the leather.

The boots began to make large strides towards the doorway. Grade, resisting the advance, threw himself upon the floor, but the lower halves of his legs continued their relentless march, as rigid as iron rods, heedless of Grade's shouts as they dragged the rest of his body into the front garden. His fingertips grasped at the paving stones and gravel for some traction against the dogged treads of the haunted, boggy boots. With each step forward, the flesh on the back of his head tore. His red wounds gushing and his body deep in the grip of pain, Grade struggled to his feet and, while still pale in fear of where the boots would take him, he resigned himself to their will.

The boots marched to the crossroads, a midway point between the town to the right and the boglands to the left. They were still at the crossroads for a moment as if considering their direction. It struck him then that the boots might be on their journey to the bog and the body of his slain brother-in-law, and he began to call out for help. Grade, unravelling in panic and pain, begged the boots for mercy. The stillness of the boots became as eerie as when they were in motion, and just when Grade thought the ordeal was over, they again began to twitch and make motion towards the town.

Grade was marched through the streets, and his fellow townspeople watched him as he walked in jarring motions, crying out for forgiveness. When the boggy boots turned the corner to the Garda station, filled with shade'ogs, Grade realised the fate that awaited him. As they drew closer, he began to call out his confession of the slaying of his brother-in-law. Hearing his cries and words of admission, the shade'ogs rose quickly and dashed towards him, grabbing him by shoulder and under-rib to ensure he would not run away. As soon as they had lifted him, the lacers untied themselves and fell lax, and the boots dropped from his feet. The dead man in the bog had released his grip. Having chosen justice instead of vengeance at the crossroads, he released Grade.

That evening Johnny left town, having never heard the news of Grade's confession nor of the boots he once owned and their torment.

Sometimes at night, when the air is still and the children of that town are safe and snug in their beds, a man's voice rolls out from the bog, lamenting his early demise and searching for someone else to wear his boots so he might again walk the land he loved so much.

Hungry grass

Crōlušk sirk

Life and death should be equally respected and any passing marked with its own honoured acknowledgement. In my community there are five deaths, which we call the sorrowful deaths, that many feel to be particularly abhorrent, deaths that are against the laws of nature and of community. It is believed that some who die in the following ways are barred from the path onward until there has been a reckoning. To leave lonely is a judgement on your kindred who may have abandoned you. To lose your last breath having not spoken the healing words of resolution leaves the dead and the living without rest from that shared conflict. And to die with a malicious deception in your heart is a betrayal of another and yourself. To pass on thirsty or hungry is also an indictment of those who could have helped carry the burdens of life. If a soul crush-auin to the edges of another realm with an empty stomach or parched lips, the family who remains often gifts a bounty of food to those in need in hopes that it will comfort the living and the dead. Items of comfort are often left by the graveside, and libations poured with a loose hand as part of the ongoing relationship between many Mincéirí and their deceased loved ones.

The Great Famine was not the only time of hunger, but it is the time that most remember. During the Gorta Mór, so many died that the graveyards were filled, new ones were formed and sometimes people were just buried where they fell, unmarked but held in the memory of local people.

Speaking even now of the collective history of this island, it is the Famine that comes to mind. But there was hunger before and hunger remains today.

When the elder Mincéirí were young and travelling across the lush land or stony roads, all those who were among their group would be sure to place a small peck of bread in their pocket as they journeyed. It could simply be for something to eat if the road was longer than expected or to give to a fellow wanderer, for the rules of hospitality are clear and a refusal to share any excess food you have brings great shame. It was also believed that grains of the bread could be sprinkled upon the ground above those who had died hungry so they would rest easy in their earthy beds.

The fear gorta, or the hungry man, is said to reach out beyond the grave in his craving, and can take over the mind and appetite of those who step upon it. There are many tales of people experiencing unexpected surges of hunger so strong they eat the grass about their feet and even devour the flesh of their very own fingers. This tale of hunger is from a kind neighbour, Old Lawrence, who passed while I was in the rising years of my teens.

Old Lawrence seemed moody and abrupt until you got to know him. He had a heart like a polished ruby and his brisk voice was a thin spider's weave, which entranced his listeners. He delighted in company and in the sharing of knowings. Beside the gable end of his home, there is a lamp post that shines apricot-toned light. On the darkening evenings we were allowed to wander as far as it, but not beyond. One day, while playing a mildly successful game of yard rounders along the pathways of Tirboy, I heard Old Lawrence in the throes of telling a tale, and much to the annoyance of most of those present, I begged him to return to the beginning. I was quickly and easily forgiven by the kind neighbours listening as he started his tale again for me, the youthful clod I was. I understand now, as I did then, that this was the highest expression of kindnesses. His home, many a year since his departure, is still known by his name and this tale is one I share in his memory.

There was a Mincéirí family whose roads were usually north of the isle but who once found themselves along the eastern lands of Wexford for Carmen's Fair. Their journey there was a soft one, as if the road itself was made of eiderdown and the wind a warm-handed guide along the way.

On arriving they sought out a haven to build a fresh molly and quickly found a field that trailed down to the coastline, edged in stones of warm pink and dusty grey, weaving in and out along the beach line like the undulating string of a just-plucked bow made from the silver kisses of horse foam. There were no recent marks of previous mollys, ants marching, nor well-worn animal tracks, the signs of a busy field. It held a slight slope, so any rainfall would run smoothly to the sea. The only unusual thing was that there was nothing but grass growing in it. No flowers or tree saplings were to be seen, nor did plants of any other sort thrive within its boundaries, but the family thought nothing of it.

Before they had chosen their field, as they passed through the parish, they had crossed paths with several locals who were happy to see them coming and welcomed the wares they had brought to sell. This, however, took a colder turn once they built their molly in an empty corner of the field. Though careful not to intrude on the pathways of man and animal, the neighbours turned frosty and began to ignore them.

The first night they rested, the crescent moon hung low in the sky and the stars drifted slowly above the tent and wagon. The world was filled with its own sleeping silence until voices were heard outside of the tent, calling out towards any that would hear them. The voices, while distinctly human, carried no clear words to the ears of the listening family. They alternated between earthy cracking and rumbling and high shrill screams. When the family awoke fully to the cries, they left the tent but found no one waiting in need by the fire. They called out but heard no reply, nothing but the natural awakenings of the coming morning.

The next day a child from a neighbouring house wandered towards the family and was given a small cup of tea by the fire. He was filled with curiosity about the new family and peppered them with questions of where they came from, who they knew and why they were staying in that field when it was full. The family, bemused, had not quite finished answering the spray of questions about their kith and kin and the roads they had travelled when the young gocklyn's mother arrived and, without a word of thanks or introduction, whisked the child off home. As they left, the woman did not let her son walk along the grass towards the small, pebble-filled pathways that cut through the field, but instead carried him, as if not wishing for his feet to touch the earth that the family were living on.

The Mincéirí family thought this unusual, but having had their own experiences of unkind neighbours and distrusting locals over the years, took no real alarm in it, as no quarrel was had in the mother taking home her own child.

That second night the family were again awoken by the moans and groans outside the tent, and they soon cast aside the heavy canvas to see who was outside and what help they might need. They wondered if the voices were carried by the sea wind and if the calls were coming from an island out of sight or a ship, unlit by lamp or lighthouse. They found the tuck box where they kept their food and utensils upturned and dashed about as if ransacked by some animal. An unease began to grow in the family. Was the field, while safe to the eye, not quite as welcoming as they had thought?

As the morning sun cracked through the horizon, the family's unease began to break and they busied about their day, making fresh tinware and picking flowers to dry for the locals, who may wish to exchange them for coin or food. During the labours of the day, the family decided that they would rest only one more night in the field before leaving. While no harsh words had been said against them, they felt the uneasiness there, the lack of welcome, the sense of being watched by those unseen eyes, and there was something indescribable in their conversations that was nonetheless palpable.

That night again they were awoken by moans and groans outside of the tent. Expecting this, the father had decided not to undress but to stay awake and alert in case he might catch sight of local youths having fun at their expense. It was a notion neither the mother nor father really believed but had kept alive in their conversations to protect their wandering thoughts from going to stranger places. He had stayed up by lamp light, his eyes on his sleeping family and his ears to the world outside their small home.

As soon as he heard the mumbles and motions, he jumped to his feet and said a blessing of care and safety for his family before he left the tent in search of the sounds' sources. The mother, not wishing to upset the children, pretended to be still sleepy, despite her heart beating like the tail of a caught salmon, and wrapped her arms around them in a tight embrace of minding and rest.

Soon the father returned, with annoyance on his face and vexation snarling from his nostrils, explaining that the horse and hounds were gone. The cob was a trusted family friend and long companion on their travels, and the hounds he had reared by hand from birth. They must have wandered off this strange field by instinct, spooked by the unnatural air. He had not heard their leaving – no barks nor heavy hooves – so they must not have gotten far, he said. He could not wait until morning to search for them and bring them home. Taking his hat and once again blessing his children, the man left in search of the animals.

The moaning continued unabated. Soon one voice among all the rest emerged close to their tent, and for the first time the mother and children, who remained inside the loban, could clearly understand the words: 'Hungry . . .', 'Starving . . .', 'Hungry . . .' An arm appeared through the flap in the entrance. Slowly and in a soft motion, the hand outstretched. The mother and the older child shrank back against the straw at the back of the tent. The younger child, however, confused and thinking the arm was that of his hero, Daddy, having returned hungry, took a peck of bread from the pocket of his pants, which were lightly folded at the head of his bed, and reached out to hand it over. As his small hand, clutching the crust, came close to the weird limb, the mother was shook into action and let out a deep roar. She swept him back and wrapped him in her arms, huddling back with her little brood, eyes fixed on the strange hand as the fallen bread rolled towards the bed.

The flesh of the arm, which had been fresh and pink when it first intruded, became grey and dull as they watched in terror. The skin began to stretch tight across the bone, the muscle underneath bundling by the elbow. As it reached closer to the family, they could see the skin drying and cracking. With every inch it advanced, it unravelled a little more, and the reek of putrid meat filled their small home. Soon the flesh began to fall away, leaving only the wrappings of a few veins around the chalky bone as it reached closer and closer to them. The mother screamed, enough to rock the lamp by the bedside, and as her cry echoed and sang against its metal, the arm withdrew quickly as if yanked back by its unseen owner. For a moment, there was an eerie silence.

Soon, however, the moans and groans began again outside of the tent, growing from small whispers to a howling hurricane. The mother and her children stayed pressed together, hands clamped over their ears, eyes wide open in fear. Suddenly, the silhouettes of skulls were pressing against the canvas of the tent, their sharp contours outlined, jaws open, sockets empty.

Fleshless fingers moved up and down the tent, picking and scraping like rats in waves of movement, searching for a hole to pick at or a snarl in the weave to unravel. Long teeth pressed taut against the fabric, pushing down towards the children and their mother, the cloth stretching to tearing point. The mother sat rocking back and forth with her children, shouting out words of prayers between the catching and losing of her breath. The howls continued to roar through the molly, as if a great beast had been wounded.

The mother took the peck of bread from the floor, threw it like a dagger through the folds of the canvas and shrieked, 'Take it!'

She prayed to herself and to any who might hear her through the screaming chaos: 'Let them take it and eat of it and they'll have no more.'

Then, in a moment, it was all gone.

There were no hands against the tent, no faces pressed upon the fabric, no howls and moans filling the air with terror. The only sounds were the family's muffled sobs and hitching breaths. They stayed still and listening until the morning light began to break through the gap in the tent flap. The camp was as still as winter's ice and not even the wind could be heard blowing.

Once dawn came and the air began to feel warmer and awake with the scents of morning, they smelled too the drifting of smoke and heard the clinking of cans and the cracking of a fresh fire. The mother drew back the canvas and peered outside. She saw her husband, ignorant of the happenings of the night, kneeling by the flames making breakfast. He began to chat of his own night-time adventure, of finding the horse and hounds, and with them a hare.

The wife quickly left the tent with a tight grasp on each of her children. She explained what had befallen them just hours before. She handed one child to her husband and picked up the other herself and insisted that they leave that very moment. They took their cart, horse and hounds and left the tent as it was standing and the food bubbling on the fire. As they left, the mother called back over her shoulder that the dead could have it, shelter for their nights and food for their days.

As they turned the corner of the road, the field falling out of view, they saw the neighbour's child along the boreen's edge. He waved at them as they passed, his bright sparrow eyes tracing their movement as they left, unsurprised at their leaving. A shiver ran down the backs of the parents, and they were thankful to no longer be upon the hungry grass of that unholy field. After some time on the road, they found fresh shelter among their own. Friends and family rummaged and brought in a spare canvas, new hazel rods for the loban frames. Those who carried care and kindness for the tormented family traded many of their own pots until they had what they needed to wander at their own pace and direction again.

From that day, the family and their people will only gather, when given a choice, in a field bursting with plant life, for a field barren but for grass could be a Famine grave, its dead still so hungry they eat back all growth but the grass in the sod above them. When the family gather in any new place, they give to those who may be there but not seen, and often throw bread with thankful hands to the birds of the field and the animals of the woods. For a well-fed friend, living or dead, is better than a hungry one.

The lantern
Granlum n'okol

There is a strip of land along one the beaches of the Galway coast, and when passing it my father would always point out the spot along the dunes where a small squat pile of stones stands. He would tell us that it was once a chair, granite and sandstone for its legs and a thick slab of slate for its seat. It has weathered the coming of winters and the heights of many a summer, and this is the tale of she who sat upon it.

There once was a couple, Nor and Róg, youthful and bright. They courted in January and married in May and they lived in a small thatched cottage not far from the tides of the ocean. Nor, a Mincéir beoir, was a weaver and spinner with fine skill and an eye for beauty, and Róg was a fisherman from the island who rose early with a trusted net and never came home without enough food for them both and more left over to be sold at the market.

They lived happy lives, uncomplicated, in the comfort of each other's company. While there were no children under the shelter of their thatched roof, there was no lack of love or laughter between them. They had each other and in having each other they were a family unto themselves. They were well liked in the village, and people were drawn to the warm chair beside their hearth. They both enjoyed the company of their neighbours. Róg played bodhrán and Nor sang sweetly, and so their evenings were filled with merriment and music.

This contentment continued for nine whole years until one September evening there came a rent in that simple rhythm. Róg had turned his boat for the shore when there was an unexpected swell. Waves grew in force and current and the water rose up and overturned his boat, swallowing it in a single ebb. Nothing was found of Nor's beloved, no boat, no oar, neither boot nor jumper, nothing except for the single brass lantern that he used in the darker months to ensure he was on course for land.

The lantern was battered, and cracks spread across its door like silver webbing. It became the focus of Nor's love and attention. By day it stayed on a simple wooden cabinet beside her bedside, the drawers of which held the neatly folded wedding suit of her husband, with his Sunday best shoes. At night, it took on another role.

She took to wearing black for a year as was the practice. But when the day came to break with colour, Nor stayed with the shade. This was considered unwise because the living, if unrelenting in their grief, can hold the dead on the threshold and twist them into something unnatural. A door kept ajar can let the dead back, but not as they once were, for death changes us all.

After the sea had taken her husband, Nor's work had dried up. There had been more than one sea casualty over the years, and many locals were wary of the makings of childless widow women, fearful that their loss and pain would be stitched and woven into the garments, that the knots would be crags of sorrow and the purls tattings of woe. This unease was given greater weight by her continued wearing of the widow's garment.

Without labour to occupy her evenings or the company of him to whom her heart had given itself, she would take the lantern and wander to the shore, and as the folds of night dropped around her, she would light it. As she sat there, looking out into the distance, she longed for sight of her husband, the lantern by her side shining out though the dark like a lighthouse calling him home. As each night ended and the sun broke the horizon, she would return to her bed, feeling as if she was losing another strand of his memory, despite her nightly watch.

Some of her neighbours knew better than to hold back much-needed labour and coin for sake of superstition, and their concern for her grew on hearing of how she still sat nightly on the beach in hopes of sight of he who had been claimed by the ocean. They took to sitting with her and listening as she recalled the days of their romance, of the dreams they had planned and the journeys they would have taken. They had hopes that their company could thaw her cold, rigid pain and usher her back to the living world.

A petition was passed on quietly to the local bishop, who too had heard of her nightly tribute, and an order for a crisp new altar cloth was made and she the chosen creator of it. News of the work brought with it the assurance of shillings and florins. Her larder, which had grown bare, could be filled high with food, and the fireplace, which had heard only the crackling of wood and seen only the plumes from half-turned turf, would have red-hot coal to fill it.

She was relieved but knew that she would not be able to go to the beach and sit in lamentation. Instead she lit the lantern and sat it on her windowsill so that its flame would still reach out across the darkness, that he might see it and know she still stood in watch and wait of him.

As she worked on her spinning wheel, she thought of him and wished to see him again, when those hazy evening thoughts that were drifting in her were suddenly stalled by a loud thud by the fireplace. Turning on her seat, but still moving her hands in work, she saw a billow of smoke sweep out from the chimney. As the ash began to settle and the room became clearer, there on the stone tiles beside the hearth was a severed human leg. Despite the soot from the chimney and the cinders in the fire, it did not appear grey, but was pink in tone and ended just where the knee should be. It did not look as if it has been ripped or cut but almost as if it had been snapped right off, like a twig from a dried autumn bush.

Still she spun, unsure of what to do, her attention fixed to the rafters expecting to hear the footsteps of those who had done such a ghastly thing. She heard nothing but the natural breathing of reeds upon the beams. If it was not for the sight of a leg only a few paces from her, she would have thought it was all her own imaginings.

She heard then a clatter at the window as the wind picked up the latch and the window swung open. As it swung back to close, in came a human arm cleaved just below the shoulder. It rolled across the floor like a dusty potato fallen from its holding sack. With her heart thumping like that of an unbridled stallion, she moved closer to the wheel, focusing on the strands of wool that with each spin entwined themselves into a cord that spun on the inner bobble. Still bemused and in a stunned daze, even though she could see with the slightest of turns the severed arm and leg that now lay on her kitchen floor, she continued to spin.

As she laboured, the calming motion of the spinning wheel, which rocked back and forth, rested the racing of her mind. She looked to the comfort of the light in the lantern, which poured out, splintering in all directions from the cracks in the glass like a captured star. As she gazed at it, she noticed that behind the window in which the lantern sat, pressed against the pane, was the outline of a torso, headless and without limb. It slumped still against the frame and glass. Illuminated by the flame of the lantern, it seemed to move as the candle burned, ominous and waiting.

The wife could bear it no more. She jumped to her feet and dashed towards the door, taking only the lantern with her. As she reached out to unbolt it, she heard three loud knocks. Recoiling, she snatched back her hand, pulled the lantern closer and called out to who was there, asking why they brought such sights to her.

There was no response except three more knocks, louder and sharper, deeper and more wilful than before.

Again the wife called out in search of a voice that would answer her question, and again there only came the knocks, this time with such force that the edges of the door frame shook, struggling to hold back what was outside waiting for her. Gathering all her courage, she held up the lantern in one hand like a shield and quickly unhitched the door. Swinging it open, she stepped outside to meet that which had visited her and had brought arm and leg and torso.

There was no one there.

There was nothing but the night and the noises of nature. As she turned back to look inside her home, to see again the severed limbs, something on the floor of the porch caught her attention. As she looked down, there, beside her feet lay the head of a man, facing upwards as if it was sleeping. A scream passed her lips and rang out about her. The eyes and mouth of the head sprung open and it crowed the words 'I have come for my wife.' On hearing his voice, the shock was shook from the woman and she recognised her lost love, but he was not as he once had been. His skin was chalky grey, karst-colour, bruised and bloated, and his hair was tangled with seaweed. There was a blankness in his pale eyes and the roaring sound of the ocean poured from his gaping maw. She moved towards him, towards the threshold between life and death.

Next day she visited the local parish, bringing the finished cloth with her, laying it with care on the table of the bishop, telling him in gleeful abandonment, much to his horror and the wringing of his hands, of her husband's unusual return. That evening, those neighbours who cared for her came to visit to stretch out the tale and what worries it spoke of. But they found her home empty and seemingly undisturbed, except that the lantern, never far from her hands, was nowhere to be found. What went unnoticed was that the cabinet beside her bed, with its drawer left open, was bare and empty, void of her husband's shoes and Sunday best.

She was never seen again, but whispered rumours of the tale continued among those kind neighbours and their descendants. And sometimes, when the moon shines just right and the sea flows in its soft uncurling, two figures holding the handles of a single lantern between them are seen wandering along the sandy beach.

Love endures but a twisted longing for the living can keep the dead from their rest. It can reach across the veils that divide the remaining from the departed, and warp a once beloved union into a monstrous match, a prison from which few can escape.

Whisht

Whisht

Growing up, I often heard 'whisht' said to a child. Sometimes it would be quickly followed by the sharp reprimand not to silence a gocklyn. Although my interest was often piqued, I never queried it. It wasn't until I started rummaging through the tales and stories of our folklore tellers that the reason was made solid and clear to me.

I had visited Willie Warde, an elder of the community, in Sligo and he gifted me this understanding of 'whisht' as we sat on a pair of metal folding chairs in the garden in front of his home. The metallic groans of my chair mumbled with my every move in and out of the telling like the eerie mewl from unseen visitors. We sipped piping-hot sweet tea and the air was thick with wisps of uncurling tobacco smoke, like church incense, an offering in the company of sharing. He told me the tale of a woman silenced so much in life that she made many scream after her death.

I have heard different versions since that first telling of her. The warning she brought has endured in our folklore. Having a voice, be it in the words of one's own heart or in the freedom of one's own actions, is a thing to protect. The silencing of a person is not only a reduction of who they are but an approach that can twist the very fibre of their being, it can stretch and sever the cords that connect us and lay a deep fetid rot and ruin in the shared foundations of our lives. A life lived in forced silence, in which the soul of a person, that kaleidoscope of expressions and inner knowings is denied voice, is a living torture that does not always end with their own passing. The Mincéirí know that a lifetime spent denigrated and twisted, with neither the comfort nor the kindness of others, rarely leads to a quiet grave.

There was once a child with a kind and caring temperament who grew up in a family whose manner was as harsh as old rusty nails. She was as different from her kin as night is from day. Their words were seldom and as sharp as summer's nettles, while she spoke in a low, rolling tone like the whispers we share in the room of a sleeping infant, and would delight in the warmth of conversation with strangers. She was fond of stories and tales and would often ask curious questions of people about their comings and goings and would take to dreaming and musing of the wonderful lives they lived. She rarely passed those along the laneways without offering the warmth of an excited greeting over her shoulder as her parents rushed her along.

As she grew, the family of the kind, talkative girl would respond to her with 'whisht' to silence her. 'Whisht!' they would say on her meeting new people and 'Whisht!' they would shout if she asked a question and 'Whisht!' they would howl if she would speak about her understanding of her life and the lives of those about her.

Soon, much sooner than most would expect, she grew to know the silence of her own held-back words and 'whisht' was said to her so very often that her own name was forgotten and it became her moniker. Her once bright spirit and her sweet mouth, always on the cusp of a smile, had become dim and cold. Where once her steps were light and dancelike, they had become slow and stolid. She lived a life of forced silence where the morning birdsong had no companion. She would silently pass her old friends on the street and would not even respond to new year blessings. She had become a stranger to those about her, and in becoming so distant to her friends and family, she became a stranger to who she once was. As the years came and went, the seasons rose and fell and old age was knotted into her bone and creased across her flesh. Death came to claim her. She passed as silently as she was forced to live.

After she was gone, those who had known her would sometimes wake at night to find her crouched down, balancing on the very tips of her toes at the heads of their beds, still dressed in her burial gown, which was stained dark from the grave soil, her hair in wet knots and tangles. She would inhale deeply with laboured breaths, as if she was sucking the air from their voices before they would find themselves, frightened and light-headed, tumbling back into a slumber. Most would meet the fresh day with hoarse crackling voices, Whisht having stolen away in death what she was denied in life. She especially longed for the voices of the young.

Generations later, in the amberlands of Cork, twilight had just descended on a shaded boreen that held to itself the full welcome of autumn with its crinkled leaves and golden tones. The air was heavy and damp as rain gently fell, the drops dancing off a lone trailer, leaving dark marks like inky flicks of music notes on manuscript paper.

The trailer was a small one with a single door at its centre that led into a cramped cooking space. There were two padded chairs to the left that could be made into a makeshift bedding area by placing a board upon the lip of both. To the right was a washing space and a narrow bed, divided from the main part of the trailer by a thin sliding door, which rarely moved with ease.

This trailer was home to a young mother and her five-year-old child. Her husband had passed in the height of his youth and his family lived all about her. Happiness had been a near constant companion while her husband lived but now, while not a stranger, had become a rarely met visitor. She found the weight of loss very heavy and so she decided that she and her child would take a few days away from the family molly and find a small speck of peace in that solitude. The loss of her husband had brought with it a sharper closeness to his family, which was welcome but often proved suffocating as she navigated her own personal seas of sorrow.

The young lackeen was brighter than the light of day and, like her mother, had in her heart a want for peace and quiet times. They spent those few days in their little refuge singing songs of soft remembrance together while they worked away at their homely chores. At night the mother would read aloud by candlelight as the child listened and gazed through the breath-fogged window to the constellations beyond, drawing lines between the stars on the glass with her little fingers. Outside the weather was cruel, but together inside they had warmth and comfort.

During one of those desolate autumn nights, the mother was woken by small fingertips tapping on the bedroom door, and her daughter's voice, calling out, 'Mommy, Mommy' like a spring swallow set behind a bush. The mother rose from her bed, shaking the slumber from her and called out, 'What is the matter, my daughter?' before drawing back the door to find her little one standing there, her small face awash with fresh tears and her hazel eyes watery with future offerings.

Wrapped in the comfort of her mother's arms, the child quickly told of a nightmare she had of Whisht. A week earlier her cousin, older in age and wiser to the ways of the world, had told her through a half-cracked smile of the creature. His words had burrowed deep in her and the tale had clicked into her child's imagination faster than the turn of a key and heavier than a set of locks. The spectre of Whisht had visited her almost hourly since it first touched her ears, growing in gruesomeness to match the fearful pain of the loss of her father.

Her mother stepped out of her bedroom, gently holding the young child's head against her hip as she moved lightly towards the kitchen, explaining how she would boil some onion cuttings in fresh milk to welcome on a kind rest. As the pot simmered, the mother coaxed the child back to bed, cradling her in her arms as she moved and singing songs of comfort.

The child, still among the bristles and brambles of her worries, told the mother of the nightmare and her cousin's tale. She told her of the woman of the moonless night, Whisht, who was so distraught at the loss of her voice that she would try to steal away the voices of others so she could be heard.

The mother spoke softly to her and reminded her that there were no monsters visiting and that she was safe, well and warm in the arms of someone who loved her. They sat for a while on the edge of the squat little bed, the mother's fingers entwined in the delicate trembling hands of her daughter, in support. The child insisted, in the pleading voice of the young, that her mother check the room for Whisht. And so she did.

First she checked under the bed, stretching out her arms and hands, tapping the floor like she was playing a drum, to call out the child's phantom, but only the well-stepped grey carpet was to be seen.

Next she checked the drawers that lined the small kitchen. The utensils rattled and clattered as she opened up the drawers and asked, 'Anyone there?' But beyond the noise of the metal clasping, there was not a single word of reply.

Last she checked the small cubic press beside the bed, the handle firm and the clasp stiff. It took more than a few pulls and jolts before it opened. As the press door creaked, she eased her body down and looked in, gasping sharply in surprise. Inside she saw her very own daughter, who she knew she had just left behind her on the bed. Whirling around, she discovered the bed was empty.

In the cabinet, the child was crumpled up and softly whimpering. Her legs were bent and jammed tight against the edges of the cabinet, her arms crossed about her body, hands tucked over each shoulder. Her head was turned, cramped against the top edge of the cupboard, with little room to catch a good breath. Unable to move her head, the child turned her eyes towards her mother. Their gazes locked on each other in terror, both holding back a scream. The mother's legs folded like the pouring of cream with the shock of realising that the child she had held by her hip as the pot of sleeping broth boiled, whose fingers her own hand had clasped while she sang some melodies of peace, was never at all her daughter. She swept the little girl out of the press and crouched over her, shielding her little one and pressing protective kisses on her damp curls.

She saw only ruffled blankets on the bed. The trailer

window was thrown ajar and moving in the wind, while shrill, sharp laughter echoed down the laneway, becoming fainter and fainter.

The mother sat clinging to her child until dawn, unmoving, afraid to let the little one go for fear she would not hold her again. She knew Whisht had visited.

Glossary of Gammon words

beoir	woman
bini komra	little dog
bini shako	small branches (twiggy)
buffer	settled person
crōlušk	hungry
crush-auin	leave quickly
gammy	malignant
gocklyn	child
gra	love
granlum n'okol	special candle (lantern)
griwog	fairy
griwog-beoir	fairy woman
guillimers	boots
kamog	walking stick

lackeen	girl
ladu	mucky soil (boggy)
leskoi	whispers
liba	bloody
loban	tent
Mincéirí	Travellers
mo gra	my love
moillhas	finger
molly	camp
réb	wisp
rírk	comb
shade'og	police
sirk	grass
stoka gresko	the low voice (whisperer)
subleens	boys
weéd	tea